HOW TO
LIVE TO
100

HOW TO LIVE TO
100

BY **MICHAEL POWELL**

PRACTICAL STRATEGIES
FOR LONGEVITY

This edition first published in Great Britain in 2016 by Allsorted Ltd, Watford, Herts, UK WD19 4BG

© Susanna Geoghegan Gift Publishing

Author: Michael Powell
Cover design: Milestone Creative
Contents design: David Onyett

ISBN: 978-1-910562-46-8

Printed in Poland

★ CONTENTS ★

47. VOLUNTEER
48. BE ECCENTRIC
49. PLAY MORE TEST CRICKET
50. WIN AN OSCAR
51. BE A FIRSTBORN BABY
52. GET A COLONOSCOPY
53. BE AN AUTUMN BABY
54. STAY IN SCHOOL
55. BE A MILDLY DEPRESSED WOMAN
56. BECOME A VEGETARIAN
57. LIVE A MEANINGFUL LIFE
58. WIN A NOBEL PRIZE
59. BE EMOTIONALLY STABLE
60. DONATE TO CHARITY
61. LIVE NEAR GREEN SPACES
62. HAVE LOTS OF FRIENDS IN YOUR DOTAGE
63. RETIRE LATER
64. HAVE LOTS OF FRIENDS IN YOUR TWENTIES
65. TRAVEL BY TRAIN
66. CUT YOUR CALORIES
67. EAT MORE SEEDS
68. EAT AN APPLE A DAY
69. BE A SEVENTH-DAY ADVENTIST
70. BE A SHORT PERSON
71. EAT ISOTOPES
72. CHECK YOUR BOWELS
73. DRINK GREEN TEA
74. HAVE THIN FRIENDS
75. BE A BREAST-FED BABY
76. BE LAZY
77. HAVE A HIGHER IQ
78. QUIT SMOKING
79. BE A LITTLE OVERWEIGHT
80. DRINK COFFEE
81. FIND GOD
82. BE A POLYGAMOUS MAN
83. EAT RED
84. LEARN A LANGUAGE
85. JOIN THE CLERGY
86. BECOME A FIREFIGHTER
87. SMILE FOR THE CAMERA
88. HAVE THE RIGHT NAME
89. COMPLAIN MORE
90. FLOSS
91. CURSE MORE
92. GOSSIP MORE
93. JOIN A CHOIR
94. CLEAN THE HOUSE MORE
95. GO COLD-WATER SWIMMING
96. EAT TURMERIC
97. BE CAREFUL WHO YOU MARRY
98. EAT YOUR BEANS
99. SIT ON THE FLOOR AND THEN GET UP AGAIN AND THEN SIT DOWN AGAIN
100. GET AN INJECTION OF YOUNG BLOOD

INTRODUCTION

With the world's population of over-sixty-five-year-olds growing by an unprecedented 800,000 a month, experts predict that centenarians will soon become as widespread as tawny owls. In fact, some scientists believe that in the near future falling off the perch may become an oversight rather than inevitable.

Take a good hard look at yourself. Are you afraid of dying? Do you want to live forever? Are you even alive? Can you rotate your overly large head by up to 270 degrees?

Life is your responsibility. The choices you make today bring about the death you have tomorrow. To borrow (and slightly change) the wise words of Tim Robbins in that film where he escapes from prison by crawling through a sewer: *get busy living...longer...or get busy dying...slightly earlier than that.*

In *How to Live to 100*, author Michael Powell's powerful, straightforward advice helps you to literally flip death the bird. He offers one hundred strategies that scientists have shown increase longevity, from gorging on blueberries and flossing regularly, to avoiding left turns, eating chocolate and guzzling litres of olive oil.

During his research, the author has spent countless hours hanging out at old people's homes, Post Office queues and Debenhams café, haranguing nonagenarians to discover the strange alchemy that has kept them off the unable-to-breathe list. He plans to publish his findings more widely just as soon as Cliff Richard has crossed over.

★ AVOID LEFT TURNS ★

In countries where motorists drive on the right, you should avoid left turns (or right turns in countries where motorists drive on the left). This is because driving across the lane of oncoming traffic is more dangerous. More people are killed making these turns, plus waiting to make the turn wastes petrol. UPS saves millions each year by giving their drivers routes which avoid left turns. So not only does avoiding left turns reduce your risk of dying, it saves petrol as well, which lowers your carbon footprint and ultimately saves the planet too.

★ PLAY BINGO ★

Researchers have discovered that pensioners can live longer by doing stuff that's easy and fun, even if it's just shopping, playing cards or going to the bingo. It doesn't matter if it doesn't get you out of breath, as Thomas Glass, assistant professor at the Harvard School of Public Health points out: 'Social and productive activities that involve little or no enhancement of physical fitness lower the risk of all causes of death as much as exercise does… It is clear from our study that social engagement can have as much effect on prolonging life as fitness activities.'

If only Jim Fixx had spent less time pounding the tarmac and learnt to play Canasta, he might still be with us today. The simple message is: *stay involved to stay alive.*

TIP 3

SHOP
★ DAILY ★

DOES GROCERY SHOPPING RANK IN YOUR TOP TEN OF FAVOURITE ACTIVITIES? OR DOES THE PROSPECT OF A MOOCH AMONG THE MELONS AND MANGOES NOT PUT A SPRING IN YOUR STEP? WHATEVER YOUR RELATIONSHIP WITH THE FOOD SHOP HAS BEEN TO DATE, IF LONG LIVING IS TOP OF YOUR LIFE GOALS, YOU MIGHT NEED TO DITCH THE WEEKLY SHOP IN FAVOUR OF A DAILY STROLL AROUND THE GROCERY AISLE OR FARMER'S MARKET.

That's according to the findings of a study carried out by a team in Taiwan in 2011, which looked at almost 2,000 seniors, aged 65 and above, over a number of years. All were active, independent, sociable and sprightly at the start of the study, but those who shopped on a daily basis proved to be a remarkable 27 per cent less likely to die over the period studied than those who didn't.

The scientists speculated that frequent shoppers were treating themselves to a daily fix of social stimulus and an invigorating hit of independence and exercise, as well as a regular supply of fresh food, which was otherwise lacking in the routines of those who stocked up once a week. This winning combination was apparently helping to keep them healthy and happy for longer.

★ HAVE CHILDREN ★

It's easy to see why exhausted parents can feel as if their lives are being shortened by the relentless responsibilities of parenting, but numerous studies have shown that the childless die younger than parents, although until the publication in 2012 of a study by Esben Agerbo of the University of Aarhus in Denmark, no one had figured out whether the absence of children caused the increase in mortality, or whether it was due to the personality traits and/or state of mind that makes people avoid procreating.

Agerbo looked at more than 20,000 couples with no previous children who sought IVF treatment between 1994 and 2008. Of these, 15,149 went on to have children and 5,354 remained childless. Subsequently, 33 of the mothers and 119 of the fathers died, compared with 56 of the childless women and 88 of the childless men. Allowing for factors such as age, education and income, the women with no children were four times more likely to die and the childless men were twice as likely. It's possible that the parents were a self-selecting group of wealthier couples, since only the first three courses of IVF were free. However, the results are startling, even allowing for this possibility.

So having children does appear to increase life expectancy – except in poor populations where more children means greater competition for scarce resources. This is supported by a 2002 study of pre-industrial Sami people in Finland which found that women with four or five children died 3.5 years earlier than those with one or fewer children.

There you have it.
Having children makes you live longer, unless you are poor.

TIP 5

TAKE
REGULAR EXERCISE

Even if you're a couch potato, it can't have escaped your attention that taking regular exercise improves mental and physical health and extends life expectancy. However, you'll be relieved to learn that you don't have to spend hours pounding the pavement or sweating on a cross-trainer to gain the benefits of being more active. Relative to time and effort expended, moderate activity has the greatest impact on all health indicators.

The US Department of Health and Human Services recommends that adults aged between 18 and 64 engage in 2.5 hours of moderate activity or 1.25 hours of vigorous activity per week (moderate means you can talk while exercising but not sing; vigorous means you are too breathless to utter more than a few words). In 2012 the National Cancer Institute (NCI) in the US published the result of its study of 650,000 adults mostly aged 40 or over. It showed an increase in life expectancy of 3.4 years for those who achieved the recommended weekly exercise, but even those who only managed half this activity still saw an increase in longevity of 1.8 years. Those who enjoyed twice the recommended levels of weekly exercise increased their lives by 4.2 years (that's merely an extra 9.5 months – or half this if you subtract the five extra days spent exercising each year for the last 30 years).

So that's good news for lazy people, because you don't have to do much exercise to gain the greatest benefits, but over-keen exercisers see diminishing returns (they also have to spend more of their lives exercising than the rest of us – time they don't get back). For the average person in their 50s or 60s, getting the recommended amount of moderate exercise halves the risk of dying from a heart attack. So, if you ignore everything else in this book, you can make the most dramatic gains simply by getting a little bit more active.

TIP 6

ATTEND YOUR OLDER SIB'S HUNDREDTH BIRTHDAY BASH

In 2001, Thomas Perls, MD, director of the New England Centenarian Study in Boston, John Wilmoth, PhD, of the University of California, Berkeley, and other researchers analysed data collected from 444 families that had at least one member living to age 100 or older. They discovered that siblings of centenarians are more likely to reach a hundred than any other group and their mortality rate is half the national average at any given age. It seems that like many things, longevity runs in families.

If you are a man with an older sibling who's just celebrated their centenary, then the fact that you were alive to see them blow out their candles is no coincidence, since you are a staggering seventeen times more likely to reach a hundred than the national average; if you're a woman then you're eight times more likely to reach this age. Dr Perls and his colleagues believe that a region on chromosome 4 is 'highly suggestive' of genetic predisposition to exceptional longevity.

LOWER YOUR
BLOOD PRESSURE

A blood pressure reading has two numbers, for example 130/80. The top number, or 'systolic', measures the pressure when your heart compresses/beats to pump blood round your body; the bottom number, or 'diastolic', measures the pressure when your heart is relaxed between beats. The higher the systolic, the harder your heart has to work to pump your blood and the greater the risk it and your blood vessels will become weaker and damaged, and the greater your risk of a stroke or heart attack.

If you have been diagnosed with high blood pressure, there are lots of lifestyle changes that you can make to reduce it, without having to resort to medication to bring it under control.

Reducing your stress is one of the biggest contributions you can make to reducing your blood pressure, but there are also several more tangible measures that are very effective. The most important of these is losing weight. Even dropping as little as ten pounds can show great improvements in your blood pressure. Also, pay attention to the distribution of your fat. Carrying too much weight around your waist increases blood pressure. Men with waists of 40 inches or greater are at risk; and women with waists of 35 inches or higher. While you're losing weight and paying greater attention to your diet, reduce your salt consumption, which is also linked to high blood pressure because it reduces your kidneys' ability to get rid of excess water in your body, so it stays in the blood, making your heart work harder.

Take regular moderate aerobic exercise that gets you out of breath. An extra three hours a week is all it takes. Also reduce your alcohol consumption. Recent studies have concluded that the increase in blood pressure caused by alcohol consumption is rapidly reversible, so even if you're a heavy drinker, you can lower your blood pressure with just a week of abstinence. Smoking also raises your blood pressure for several minutes after each cigarette, so cut down or stop smoking completely. Finally, if you are sensitive to caffeine, cut down your consumption. You can test your susceptibility by taking your blood pressure before and then half an hour after having a caffeinated drink.

TIP 8

★ NEVER SKIP BREAKFAST ★

THOSE WHO RUSH OUT OF THE HOUSE ON AN EMPTY STOMACH MAY BE GIVING UP MORE THAN BREAKFAST. THE GEORGIA CENTENARIAN STUDY ASKED A BUNCH OF OLD TIMERS ABOUT THEIR BREAKFASTING HABITS, AND THOSE OVER THE AGE OF 100 TENDED NOT TO BE THE SORT WHO GRABBED A PASTRY ON THE WAY TO WORK (WAY BACK WHEN).

Not only does a good breakfast kick-start your metabolism after a night of fasting (that's why it's called break-fast) by bringing your blood sugar level back to normal, it also sets a pattern for the rest of the day's eating. It's been shown that those who skip breakfast are more likely to eat badly during the rest of the day. It doesn't have to be fancy: just milk, cereal and a glass of orange juice. The milk alone is stuffed with calcium, vitamin A, vitamin B1, vitamin B2, vitamin B6, vitamin B12, niacin, phosphorus, potassium, iodine, magnesium and zinc.

Eating breakfast reduces the risk of a heart attack because platelets – the blood's clotting cells – are 'stickier' when you wake up in the morning, prior to eating, which is why most heart attacks occur between 7am and 12 noon. A recent study of 3,000 people who lost an average of 70 pounds and kept them off for six years, found that 78 per cent of them ate breakfast every day as part of their weight-control strategy. People who keep within a healthy body weight live longer.

Ray Kurzweil, computer scientist, inventor and director of engineering at Google and author of *Fantastic Voyage: Live Long Enough to Live Forever* asserts that in the future, everyone will live forever. He eats a 700-calorie nutrient-dense breakfast of superfoods every day as part of his cutting-edge scientific attempt to remain young and healthy indefinitely.

If you want to live forever, be more like Ray – don't skip breakfast.

TIP 9

ENJOY
★ CHOCOLATE ★

For several years, chocolate has enjoyed its reputation as a mineral- and antioxidant-rich superfood with a wide range of health benefits including increased longevity. A fifteen-year study of 470 men aged 65 and over found that men who consumed the least chocolate were twice as likely to die from a heart attack than those who consumed the most.

Chocolate in its rawest form – the cacao bean – contains more than 300 known chemicals, many of which are life enhancing, including the anti-asthmatic compounds theobromine and theyophilline. The former also helps to kill the bacteria that cause gum disease. It contains high levels of sulphur and magnesium, which are good for concentration, as well as zinc and copper. The magnesium also helps to regulate your appetite, so you feel fuller for longer. An Italian study has found that regularly consuming chocolate also increases the body's sensitivity to insulin, reducing the risk of developing Type 2 diabetes. Most important of all, chocolate contains the anti-depressant phenethylamine and the neurotransmitter anandamide which reduces stress, so you can literally eat yourself happier.

However, to gain these benefits you must eat dark, unrefined chocolate, not the kind that is laden with unhealthy levels of milk, sugar, saturated fats and artificial flavouring.

GET UP CLOSE TO FLOWERS

WHEN WAS THE LAST TIME YOU TREATED YOURSELF TO A BUNCH OF YOUR FAVOURITE FLOWERS? ACCORDING TO RECENT RESEARCH, IT'S A HABIT WE SHOULD ALL BE GETTING INTO MORE OFTEN.

Anxiety and depression present increasing problems across all age groups. Science already tells us that that's not helping our longevity: sustained stress attacks our sense of wellbeing, robs us of our sleep, affects our diet and nutrition and weakens our immune system.

So to turn that around, clear your heart and mind and give your immune system a life-extending boost, get up close to some flowers. Wander through a flower market, take a stroll through a city park or treat yourself to a bunch of your favourite blooms. The colour and scent not only help lift your mood, they reduce your anxiety levels, boost concentration and help improve your memory, according to one study undertaken at the University of Michigan, which found a memory increase as high as 20 per cent after spending time in the presence of flowers.

Other studies have found that not only does the presence of flowers in your home or workplace help you de-stress, but it also induces a greater sense of security, leaving you feeling more optimistic. All of this is great news, as it helps your body churn out a healthy dose of happy hormones and lowers your blood pressure.

TIP 11

EAT BIRD'S NEST SOUP

Made from the hardened saliva of endangered cave-dwelling swiftlets and harvested with difficulty and significant personal peril using long bamboo poles, bird's nests have been eaten by the rich and privileged in China for the best part of a thousand years. Although there have been fears about over-harvesting, new methods of 'farming' the nests in purpose-built structures have helped to regulate trade – though not, it seems, to decrease the mystique, nor indeed the price, of this highly prized delicacy.

The nests, called *yan wo* in Chinese, are sometimes referred to as 'the caviar of the east', and although they can be eaten in a variety of dishes, both sweet and savoury, the most famous is bird's nest soup. To make the soup, the nest is dissolved in stock, usually chicken, and it gives the soup a thick, jelly-like texture. Flavouring comes from any added ingredients rather than the nest itself.

In common with every other expensive delicacy found in various cultures' traditional medicine, the dish is credited with a host of health-giving properties, from improved concentration and enhanced lung function to reducing the signs of ageing – as well as the inevitable increased libido.

So what's the proof that it makes you live longer? Unfortunately, this widely touted claim has not been supported by any major clinical trials. In fact, some scientists argue that the insipid ingredient has no proven health benefits at all. Others claim that the food contains a substance that stimulates cell division and enhances tissue repair. All that can be said with any certainty is that it consists of about 50 per cent protein and 30 per cent carbohydrate and contains the minerals calcium, iron, magnesium and potassium, and that one hundred grams of bird's nest will cost you more than a year's gym membership.

It is well known that rich people live longer than poor people, so it's easy to see how chowing down on expensive bird saliva became conflated with increased longevity; although it has the opposite effect on the lifespan of those who harvest the nests. But so-called elixirs of life have always been hard to harvest, so that all feeds into its mythology.

If you do decide to prioritise eating bird's nest soup over say, buying a cross-trainer, then the white nests, containing fewest feathers, are the most sought after, leading disreputable suppliers to bleach their product to fetch a higher price. So take advice from your local traditional Chinese medicine centre rather than buying a sackful of dazzling white nests on the Internet.

TIP 12

EAT
MEDITERRANEAN

Numerous studies have linked a Mediterranean diet with longer life and reduced incidence of chronic diseases, especially major cardiovascular diseases. It's no accident that some of the populations with the longest lifespans in the world live along the Mediterranean coast. The diet is rich in olive oil, pulses, beans, nuts, tomatoes and other fresh fruit and vegetables, fish and unrefined grains, swilled down with a moderate intake of alcohol.

One of the latest studies appeared in the *British Medical Journal*, following 4,676 middle-aged women enrolled in the Nurses' Health Study, which has been tracking the health and lifestyles of more than 120,000 registered nurses in the US since 1976. The study found that women following a Mediterranean diet had longer telomeres at the ends of their DNA strands, which is associated with longer life (see page 84 for an explanation of this mechanism).

The researchers found, however, that it was the diet as a whole that had this beneficial effect, rather than one specific component. They intend to follow up the study by charting the effects of the Mediterranean diet on men, but it would be a fair bet to assume that the overall health benefits will be similar.

TIP 13

★ GET LAUGHING ★

Anecdotally, the many beneficial effects of laughter are well known: raising our spirits, helping us to forget our troubles and bringing people together. However, there is also lots of clinical evidence that laughter plays a key role in health and longevity and can positively affect a diverse range of illnesses from arthritis and heart disease to high blood pressure and diabetes. One fifth of National Cancer Institute treatment centres in the US offer humour therapy, which involves watching, reading and listening to mirth-inducing material.

Researchers at the Moriguchi-Keikinkai Hospital in Japan showed a Charlie Chaplin film and a weather documentary to two groups of breastfeeding mothers whose babies had been diagnosed with eczema. The women who watched the comedy were found to have higher levels of melatonin in their breast milk, which had a positive effect on their babies' allergic reactions.

Happiness and laughter have been shown to increase the activity of natural killer cells in the body, to lower the stress hormone cortisol and to release endorphins, the body's natural pain killers. The physical act of laughing also increases oxygenation of the blood by giving the lungs and abdominal muscles a mini workout and temporarily raising the heart rate (in a positive way). A 2005 study by the University of Maryland School of Medicine in Baltimore indicates that laughter appears to cause the endothelium – the inner lining of blood vessels – to dilate, allowing increased blood flow. The opposite effect – vasoconstriction – occurs in response to stress. So not only does laughter help to keep blood vessels elastic and resilient, it also reduces inflammation in the body, which is linked to a wide range of illnesses. Another Japanese study found that watching a comedy show even lowered levels of a protein involved in the progression of the kidney disease diabetic nephropathy.

The poster boy for laughter therapy remains the now-deceased American political journalist Norman Cousins, who famously managed the crippling pain of ankylosing spondylitis by watching hours of comedy on television (although he also took massive intravenous doses of vitamin C). In 1979 he published his seminal book about the experience, which was subsequently made into the film *Anatomy of an Illness*, in which he eulogised: 'I made the joyous discovery that ten minutes of genuine belly laughter had an anaesthetic effect and would give me a least two hours of pain-free sleep.'

★ BE RICH ★

For decades it has been established beyond all doubt that on average, richer people live longer than poor people. In fact, this phenomenon even has a name: 'the wealth gradient in mortality'. Furthermore, the gap between the longevity of the rich and poor is growing. Between 2001 and 2014, the richest five per cent of Americans gained an extra three years of life, while the poorest five per cent showed no improvement. Richer people tend to exercise more, have more hobbies, enjoy closer relationships and crucially, live longer because they have the luxury of making healthier life choices.

A recent study printed in the *Journal of the American Medical Association* showed that the age gap between the richest and poorest one per cent of men in the US was almost fifteen years. But when quality of life is taken into account, the figure is even higher. A recent study by the Office for National Statistics in the UK split England and Wales into 30,000 areas and then ranked them according to levels of deprivation, including factors such as crime, average income and education. Then it used existing mortality figures to make life expectancy projections about 'Healthy Life Expectancy' – the time spent leading a full and active life in good health. In the most deprived area in the study – Jaywick in Clacton-on-Sea in Essex – men were projected to enjoy 52.1 years of full and active life and women a few months extra, while in an area just outside Chorleywood in Hertfordshire, the least deprived, men enjoyed an extra 19.3 years of full active life, and women a year longer still.

British scientists have also discovered that rich people tend to have higher levels of the hormone DHEAS (dehydroepiandrosterone sulphate), a steroid produced naturally by the brain, adrenal glands and sexual organs, responsible for regulating the stress response.

So the message is clear: wealthy people are healthier. But before you rush out to buy a lottery ticket, this benefit does not apply to suddenly acquired riches. Economists call this 'positive income shock' and unfortunately the statistics show that this reduces your life expectancy. You've got more chance of being struck by lightning than winning the lottery jackpot, but seventy per cent of winners blow their fortune within seven years and there are scores of true stories about lottery winners living fast and dying well before their time.

EMIGRATE TO ANDORRA

This principality in south-western Europe, sandwiched between France and Spain, has a population of around 70,000 and the highest life expectancy in the world. It must be a combination of genetics, living at altitude, a Mediterranean diet and its 'tax haven' status. If you're considering moving, here are the top twenty countries which just can't kick the oxygen habit.

Rank	Country	Life expectancy	Rank	Country	Life expectancy
1	Andorra	83.47	11	Canada	79.56
2	Macau	81.69	12	Iceland	79.52
3	San Marino	81.23	13	Italy	79.14
4	Japan	80.8	14	Gibraltar	79.09
5	Singapore	80.17	15	Cayman Islands	79.03
6	Australia	79.87	16	Monaco	78.98
7	Guernsey	79.78	17	Liechtenstein	78.95
8	Switzerland	79.73	18	Spain	78.93
9	Sweden	79.71	19	France	78.9
10	Hong Kong	79.67	20	Norway	78.79

TIP 16

DRINK
★ RED WINE ★

During the eighties, researchers were baffled by the observation that French people enjoy a diet that is high in saturated fats but have a relatively low incidence of coronary heart disease. They called it the 'French Paradox'. Since then, numerous studies have found that moderate consumption of red wine protects against heart disease and cancer and is linked to longevity.

The secret protective ingredient in red wine isn't the alcohol, although this plays a part; it's the antioxidants it contains, especially resveratrol which is found in grape skins and seeds. Resveratrol acts on several parts of the body to improve longevity. It activates the longevity-related protein sirtuin 1 (SIRT1). In fact, according to David Sinclair, Harvard Medical School professor of genetics, 'In the history of pharmaceuticals, there has never been a drug that binds to a protein to make it run faster in the way that resveratrol activates SIRT1.' Resveratrol also improves insulin sensitivity (reducing the risk of diabetes) and improves mitochondria function, which is also linked to ageing.

So raise a glass of red to the French, but if you don't like wine, cranberries, mulberries, lingonberries, peanuts and pistachios are also good sources of resveratrol.

MINIMISE DANGEROUS CHEMICALS

Few people are aware of the lethal cocktail of toxic chemicals in our environment, nor the harm that is being caused by their daily accumulation in our bodies. Even scientists are unable to pinpoint all the ways the thousands of chemicals we're exposed to interact inside our tissues and cells. We live in a highly polluted world, but we can improve our chances of enjoying good health and longevity by educating ourselves in the dangers of these hidden killers so we can reduce or eliminate them from our lives.

The World Health Organization (WHO) has called for action on 10 chemicals of 'major health concern' including air pollution, benzene, dioxins and dioxin-like substances, lead, mercury and hazardous pesticides. These global issues are largely beyond our control, but we can reduce chemical exposure on a domestic level by learning about the contents of our food, drink, clothes, household cleaning items, carpets, furniture, consumer and personal care products.

Three things you can do immediately:
1. Where possible, avoid junk food and eat organic whole foods, free of preservatives and colouring agents.
2. Use chemical-free cosmetics, body care and cleaning products.
3. Filter your drinking water.

Now read Paula Baillie-Hamilton's book *Stop the 21st Century Killing You: Toxic Chemicals Have Invaded Our Life*.

26

DEVELOP YOUR
LEG STRENGTH

DO YOU HAVE STRONG LEGS? IF YOU DO, IT'S A GOOD INDICATOR THAT YOU ARE IN GOOD HEALTH AND YOUR FUTURE PROSPECTS LOOK BRIGHT. IF ONLY HOROSCOPES WERE AS RELIABLE AS THIS. SO RELIABLE, IN FACT, THAT A DECADE-LONG STUDY OF 324 HEALTHY FEMALE TWINS FOUND THAT LEG STRENGTH WAS A BETTER INDICATOR OF THE MAINTENANCE OF COGNITIVE FUNCTION OVER TIME THAN ANY OTHER LIFESTYLE FACTOR.

People with strong legs are, of course, a self-selecting group of active, healthy individuals with better than average longevity, because active people are healthier and have stronger legs than sedentary people, who will tend to have weaker legs. But it works both ways: if you want to improve your health, get more active, and measure your progress by testing your leg strength because the stronger your legs, the longer you will enjoy the optimal function of the stuff between your ears.

Stand-sit-stand test
Measure your leg strength and general mobility now with this simple test:
1. Stand in comfortable clothes in your bare feet.
2. Without leaning on anything, lower yourself to a sitting position on the floor.
3. Now stand back up, without using your hands, knees, forearms or sides of your legs.

Now turn the page to see how you score

Scoring
Each of the two movements is scored out of 5, with one point deducted every time a hand, knee, forearm or side of leg is used, and 0.5 points deducted for loss of balance. In a study of 2,000 patients aged 51 to 80, published in the *European Journal of Cardiology*, people who scored three or fewer points out of ten were five times more likely to die within the next six years compared with those who scored more than eight points.

★ BE RIGHT-HANDED ★

SEVERAL STUDIES HAVE SHOWN A LINK BETWEEN LEFT-HANDEDNESS AND INCREASED MORTALITY, ALTHOUGH SCIENTISTS DISAGREE ON THE DIFFERENTIAL AS WELL AS THE MANY FACTORS, BOTH GENETIC AND ENVIRONMENTAL, THAT PLAY THEIR PART.

During the 1980s American psychologists Stanley Coren and Diane Halpern conducted a famous study into 1,000 recently deceased people in California and found that on average the right-handers lived nine years longer than the left-handers. Since then their methodology has been discredited, as they were from a generation that was forced to become right-handed during childhood. This has led many since to dismiss the left-hander shortened lifespan as a myth.

However, the fact remains that many other studies have linked left-handedness to higher incidence of allergies, epilepsy, learning difficulties, drug abuse, attempted suicides and autoimmune diseases. Trying to function in a world designed for right-handed people also leads to more minor accidents.

An early study of baseball players showed that the mean life span of left-handers was nine months shorter than that of right-handers. Psychologists at Durham University also analysed 3,000 first-class bowlers from 1864 to 1983 listed in the *Who's Who of Cricketers*. The left-handed bowlers had an average lifespan of 63.5 years, compared with 65.5 years for the right-handed players.

A recent Dutch study printed in the journal *Epidemiology* followed 12,178 middle-aged women for 13 years. During this time 252 participants died: the deaths of left-handers was 40 per cent higher than expected and they suffered a 70 per cent higher incidence of cancer, twice the deaths from breast cancer than expected and a five-fold increase in colorectal cancer.

Scientists are still trying to unpick the statistics, but there does appear to be a link between being left-handed and shortened life.

TIP 20

CHEW
YOUR FOOD WELL

CHEW YOUR FOOD UNTIL IT'S LIQUEFIED AND ENJOY BETTER HEALTH STRAIGHT AWAY. DIGESTION BEGINS IN YOUR MOUTH. YOU SECRETE SALIVA WHICH COATS YOUR FOOD WITH DIGESTIVE ENZYMES, INCLUDING AMYLASE (WHICH HELPS YOUR BODY BREAK DOWN STARCH) AND LIPASE (WHICH HELPS YOUR BODY DIGEST FATS). SALIVA PRODUCTION ALSO DIGESTS THE BACTERIA THAT LEAD TO PLAQUE BUILD-UP.

As your teeth break the food down, it covers a wider surface area, so that when it reaches your stomach, your digestive enzymes and stomach acid can work on it more effectively, breaking down the carbohydrates into simple sugars and digesting fats into fatty acids. The more you chew, the easier job your intestines have to extract the micronutrients.

Chewing longer also makes eating a more conscious process. Too many of us shovel food into our bodies while distracted by the television, or rush a meal on the go and stuff ourselves to the point of discomfort. It takes 20 minutes for the stomach to signal the brain that you're full, so chewing more means eating more slowly and consuming less food. It makes eating a vital conscious process and you more mindful of what and how you are consuming.

EAT SEVEN WALNUTS EVERY DAY

Walnuts are extremely good for your health, and in fact some nutritionists refer to them as the king of superfoods. They contain protein, healthy fats, fibre, plant sterols, antioxidants and many vitamins and minerals including heart-healthy vitamin E, and magnesium, which helps maintain nerve and muscle function, steady heart rhythm, support the immune system and build strong bones.

Walnuts fight cancer. In studies, feeding walnuts to mice reduced prostate cancer growth by up to 40 per cent and cut breast cancer risk in half. Walnuts protect the heart: they contain the amino acid l-arginine which reduces blood pressure. They support healthy cholesterol levels and are also loaded with essential omega-3 fatty acids which reduce inflammation and improve brain function.

Walnuts also contain several powerful antioxidants which combat age-related cell deterioration. These include the allelopathic compound juglone (which protects against liver cancer), the tannin tellimagrandin and morin (which protects against Alzheimer's disease, as well as Type 2 diabetes).

Walnuts are used in traditional Chinese medicine to aid kidney function, treat asthma and cure constipation in the elderly. They have even been shown to improve fertility in men. Simply replacing one high-calorie daily snack with a handful of walnuts has tangible health benefits.

TIP 22

★ GROW A GARDEN ★

EXPERTS CLAIM THAT GARDENING COULD PLAY A CENTRAL PART IN LIVING A LONG AND HEALTHY LIFE. IN FACT, ITS BENEFITS ARE SO SELF-EVIDENT THAT DOCTORS HAVE BEGUN TO ISSUE 'GREEN PRESCRIPTIONS' – INSTRUCTING THEIR PATIENTS TO GET OUTSIDE TO START DIGGING AND PLANTING.

Growing Health is a national project run by Garden Organic and Sustain in the UK to see how community food growing can be used by the health and social care services to promote health and wellbeing. It has developed case studies showing how gardening benefits physical and mental health and the general wellbeing of a wide range of different patient groups.

Community gardening reduces blood pressure, controls weight, increases mobility and lung function and helps to reduce social isolation, loneliness and depression. Sarah Williams, project manager for Growing Health says: 'We know that there are an array of benefits for people who get outdoors and get their hands in the soil. They include being active, getting fresh air, and meeting others. What we would now like to see is more GPs signposting their patients into these outdoor growing activities as a more cost-effective way of keeping people healthy.'

A recent Swedish study of 4,232 people over the age of 60 showed that gardening is a great alternative to high-intensity exercise for older people and that being active can reduce the risk of stroke or heart attack by 27 per cent and death by any other cause by 30 per cent.

TIP 23

LIVE ON A
★ MOUNTAIN ★

The reason for the link between health and living at altitude remains unclear, but the fact remains that people living on mountains live longer. Research by the University of Washington's Institute for Health Metrics and Evaluation shows that seven out of ten of the longest-lived counties in the US are mountain communities, including Crested Butte's Gunnison County and Aspen's Pitkin County. There is also an inverse link between altitude and obesity – the higher you live, the thinner you are likely to be.

One of the reasons for this, apart from increased activity levels, is that living at higher altitude suppresses appetite. Also, people living at altitude have a higher metabolic rate – their hearts beat faster at rest – so they burn more calories as they go about their daily lives, even before walking uphill and downhill increases their activity. People at higher altitude also have more blood vessels in their heart and their cells have adjusted for a lower level of oxygen.

Researchers recognise that increased health may be partially explained by self-selection. Healthier, more active people are attracted to mountain towns, and sick people would be more likely to leave those areas in favour of lower ground with a greater concentration of hospitals. But the link remains even after these considerations have been factored out.

TIP 24

PROTECT YOURSELF FROM THE SUN

The sun's ultraviolet (UV) radiation is a proven human carcinogen. Skin cancer is the most common form of cancer in the UK and one in five Americans will develop skin cancer in the course of a lifetime. In fact, more people develop skin cancer because of tanning than develop lung cancer because of smoking.

It is largely preventable if you use a broad-spectrum sunscreen – which blocks both UVA and UVB rays – with an SPF of 15 or higher. If you spend a day on the beach during the summer, you should aim to use an entire 150ml bottle of sun cream. But you should also be using some form of sun protection such as an SPF moisturiser on your face and other exposed skin even during the winter months.

Sun exposure can also damage your eyes and the sensitive skin around them, increasing your risk of cataracts, macular degeneration (the leading cause of blindness in older people), pingueculae and pterygia (growths on the eye's surface) and basal cell carcinoma, so make sure your sunglasses provide 100 per cent protection from UV radiation as well as high-energy visible (HEV) radiation (which can also damage the retina), and are preferably of a close-fitting wraparound style.

TIP 25

TAKE AFTERNOON NAPS

IN 2007, A STUDY OF 23,681 MEN AND WOMEN AGED BETWEEN 20 AND 86 CONDUCTED BY EPIDEMIOLOGISTS AT THE UNIVERSITY OF ATHENS MEDICAL SCHOOL AND THE HARVARD SCHOOL OF PUBLIC HEALTH FOUND THAT SIESTAS WERE CORRELATED WITH LOWER RATES IN FATAL HEART ATTACKS, ESPECIALLY IN WORKING MEN.

Overall, regular napping, at least three days a week, was associated with a 37 per cent reduction, while occasional napping saw a 12 per cent reduction. Among working men who took midday naps, there was a 64 per cent reduced risk of death compared with a 36 per cent reduced risk among non-working men.

However, too much of a good thing is usually bad for you: an earlier 2003 Israeli study found that long siestas (over 2 hours) were correlated with increased mortality among men and those with chronic health problems. So keep your napping down to between 20 and 40 minutes a day, otherwise you may be doing yourself harm, as well as interfering with your night-time sleep.

TIP 26

LOOK ON THE
BRIGHT SIDE

If, like Woody Allen, you have a tendency to see life as a bleak choice between 'the horrible and the miserable', there are solid scientific reasons why you should consider adopting a glass-half-full outlook. A study conducted in 2015 by research scientists at University College, London discovered that a pessimistic outlook has a significant impact on survival rates of heart-attack sufferers. The scientists carried out psychological testing of a group of patients who had suffered their first heart attack and found that the optimists were twice as likely to be healthy four years later, when compared to the pessimists.

The study analysed some of the reasons for this, to find that among those patients who had been smokers, the optimists were far more likely to have quit a year down the line. They were also twice as likely to have sustained a healthier diet, richer in fruit and vegetables.

In fact, more than 80 worldwide scientific studies into the health benefits of seeing your glass as half full conclude that, even where other social and economic factors are accounted for, optimists survive not only heart disease better, but also cancer and a range of other diseases.

EAT BLUEBERRIES
(and other antioxidants)

We all know that we need to eat our fruit and vegetables for optimal health but scientists are beginning to discover that the humble blueberry has a significant impact on the longevity of numerous species across the animal kingdom. Fruit flies, for instance, fed a blueberry-rich diet, have been found to live on average 28 per cent longer than their blueberry-deprived fellows.

What's more, studies have found that the polyphenols and other nutrients found in plentiful supply in blueberries not only help you live longer, but think, look, see and move better too, reduce wrinkles, and maintain bone density, skin elasticity, brain response time and retina health. Other berries, particularly cranberries and strawberries, have similar benefits.

But for real longevity, look to what one doctor, Dr Mark Hyman, has described as 'the mother of all antioxidants', a miraculous molecule called glutathione. Linked by a staggering 89,000 scientific studies to the prevention of ageing, dementia and Alzheimer's, cancer, heart disease and even autistic spectrum disorder, glutathione is produced naturally in our bodies, but poor diet and lifestyle can easily leave us depleted. To replenish your supplies, tuck into garlic, onion, watercress, cauliflower, broccoli, cabbage and asparagus.

TIP 28

GO TO BED
★ EARLIER ★

Are you a night owl? Do you push bedtime closer and closer to the small hours, in pursuit of box-sets, Twitter or another glass of red? Too many of us are not getting the sleep we need. Good quality, plentiful sleep helps keep our spirits up, our waistline down and our focus sharp. It makes us more effective at work and easier to be around. It helps stave off colds and viruses, makes workouts more productive and helps keep in balance those hormones that tell our brain we're hungry.

But a good night's sleep does more than make us feel better; in the pursuit of longevity, healthy sleep habits are essential. A wealth of scientific evidence warns that the seven-hours-or-less-a-night crew are statistically more prone to work-place accidents, car crashes, heart disease and stroke, breast cancer and obesity. Little wonder, then, that those who routinely sleep for an hour or two less than their recommended seven or eight hours have a 70 per cent greater chance of death across all adult age-groups than those who generally sleep well.

BE A MODERATE
DRINKER

The scientific community has struggled for a while to decide how it feels about the relationship between drink and death. For those who still think drinking responsibly means not spilling their Pinot Noir, the news isn't good. Heavy drinkers have inevitably failed to come off well across all studies, being as much as 70 per cent more likely to die than moderate drinkers. But a study carried out in Sweden in 2014 offers a glimmer of hope, upholding the old adage about everything in moderation.

The Swedish team followed the drinking habits of a group of middle-aged drinkers over 15 years, and concluded that those who drank lightly (half a unit daily for women, a unit and a half for men) were living on average 15 to 17 months *longer* than those who didn't drink at all. The reasons for the apparent value of a moderate drinking habit are as yet unclear, with some arguing that the benefit to health may lie simply in the fact that as a social habit, an evening drink with family or friends can help reduce stress and anxiety and boost a healthy sense of wellbeing. This line of reasoning suggests that the same benefit could be found in, for example, sharing an evening stroll with your mates. A reasonable alternative, but there's no harm in rounding it off with a chilled Chardonnay.

GET ON WITH YOUR MOTHER

(or your father, sister, brother, cousins, friends)

Sometimes, the scientific pursuit of longevity has thrown up some less obvious lifestyle habits. Quit smoking, eat your greens, get your sleep – we get that. But get on well with your parents? Less obvious. However, according to an extensive study carried out in the US, a lack of strong, meaningful relationships with family and friends can be as harmful to our health and longevity as smoking 15 cigarettes a day. In fact, they found that people without meaningful relationships were 50 per cent more likely to die prematurely from any cause.

The reasons for this are hard to quantify: scientifically, in essence, it boils down to the fact that we're social beings. We are meant to live communally. Having a supportive network, being in the company of people you like and care about, is known to alleviate the kinds of stress which can impact most severely on the function of our heart, gut, insulin production and immune system. But more than that, the sense of purpose, value and usefulness that comes from caring for our nearest and dearest also contributes significantly to our immune system on a cellular level. We feel better if we feel we have a social function.

TIP 31

GET A
★ PET ★

WE'VE BEEN LIVING IN CLOSE QUARTERS WITH OUR ANIMAL FRIENDS FOR GENERATIONS AND HAVE LONG UNDERSTOOD THE VALUE OF PET OWNERSHIP TO OUR PHYSICAL AND MENTAL WELLBEING.

But in 2013, the American Heart Association finally quantified the perks of the pooch, finding conclusive evidence that dog-ownership in particular lowers our risk of coronary heart disease.

The reasons are probably two-fold: a dog gets us out in the fresh air, moving. But a dog is also more likely to offer us emotional support because it more obviously reciprocates affection. Cat-lovers may be further upset by the news that the AHA speculated that they couldn't rule out as a possibility that dog owners were more inclined towards an active, emotionally reciprocal lifestyle in the first place, making them more inclined to introduce a pup to the family than a kitten.

CHOP OFF YOUR TESTICLES

If you feel strongly about living to a ripe old age, then lopping off your love apples is a small price to pay for nearly two decades of extra nadger-free existence. This was the finding of a study of 81 eunuchs who lived in Korea between the mid-sixteenth and mid-nineteenth century.

Analysis of court records by Kyung Jin Min of Inha University of Incheon in South Korea, revealed that the eunuchs in the studied group lived on average between 14 and 19 years longer than their non-castrated peers. He concluded: 'It provides some of the most compelling evidence yet that the male sex hormone, testosterone, reduces male lifespan.'

Experiments on rats produces similar results: the removal of a rat's plums extends life by up to 27 months. One possible explanation is that amino acids in the body can be used for cell defence and repair when the burden of producing semen is removed. The Korean eunuchs were also smaller than their peers (see page 80 for the link between size and longevity) and they didn't suffer from any life-shortening venereal diseases.

Another study published in a 1969 issue of the *Journal of Gerontology* compared the life spans of 297 castrated inmates of a Kansas asylum with 735 intact inmates and observed an average increase of 13.6 years of life, with the longest-lived subjects being those who were castrated before puberty.

TIP 33

EAT LIKE CONFUCIUS:
STOP WHEN YOU ARE EIGHT PARTS FULL

If an all-you-can-eat buffet has you drooling like Homer Simpson, it really might be time to read a little more Confucius. In the decades since the rationing of the Second World War, generations have been raised on the principle that an empty plate is a good thing. The trouble is, in the West we have maintained that approach to meal times, in spite of the super-sizing of portions at every sitting, and the result is an obesity epidemic that's doing nobody any good.

The people of Okinawa in Japan have turned the Confucian principal of stopping eating when you are just short of feeling full into a way of life. In Japanese, it's called *'Hara hichi bun me'* (belly eight parts full) and it has resulted in an average daily consumption of just 1,800 to 1,900 calories on the island. Consequently, they have the world's highest population of centenarians and a typical body mass index of 18 to 22.

So if you have your eye on a long and healthy life, maybe it's time to stop stretching your belly by treating every meal as if it's your last. Take your time, enjoy every mouthful but stop before you feel full.

TIP 34

EAT MORE
★ SEAWEED ★

Ask any farmer who has ever fed their livestock seaweed and they'll tell you the same story: not only do cows, sheep and hens go crazy for the stuff, but they also thrive on it. And it isn't just farm animals: any human population in the world which has a diet rich in kelp, nori and other seaweeds thrives on the additional trace minerals it absorbs from this super-nutrient-rich food. Seaweed eaters are thriving well into old age, outliving the rest of us in the process.

Seaweed and any other vegetables grown in soil that was once below sea level are rich in one nutrient that is in scarce supply in almost all other foods: iodine. Iodine keeps your thyroid healthy, protects against breast cancers and counters the problems of inflammation associated with ageing. So not only does it help keep you healthy, it keeps you healthy for longer, extending your longevity.

One word of caution, however: the nutrients in seaweed can be in such significant supplies that they can be too good for you. Some varieties contain enough potassium to give anyone with kidney disorders palpitations. Nori, used in sushi, eaten a couple of times a week, however, is a good, safe place to start.

TIP 35

HAVE AN O-TYPE BLOOD GROUP

NOT SOMETHING YOU CAN DO MUCH ABOUT, BUT FOR THOSE OF YOU WITH AN O-TYPE BLOOD GROUP, IT'S WORTH KNOWING THAT STATISTICALLY, YOU STAND LESS CHANCE OF DEVELOPING HEART DISEASE AND MORE CHANCE OF LIVING A LONG LIFE.

That's according to a research team from the US National Institute of Health, which carried out a seven-year study of 50,000 middle-aged and elderly people in Iran. O-blood people were 15 per cent less likely to die from cardiovascular disease during the period of the study, even after other potential factors such as smoking, diet and exercise were factored out. One possible cause of the trend emerged from the study: people with O-type blood group tended to have lower levels of LDL cholesterol than those in the other blood groups, particularly those in the A-type blood group, whose LDL levels were found to be the highest.

Doctors emphasised, however, that while these results were interesting, non-O types should not feel that poor health and an early death is pre-determined: diet and lifestyle choices are still by far the biggest predictors of longevity and heart health.

STAND UP
MORE

IF THE WAY YOU EARN A LIVING MAKES IT INCREASINGLY DIFFICULT TO MAKE TIME TO TAKE REGULAR EXERCISE AND INSTEAD KEEPS YOU PINNED TO YOUR DESK FOR GREAT CHUNKS OF YOUR DAY, YOU MIGHT WANT TO TRY STANDING UP MORE OFTEN.

We already know that a sedentary lifestyle is our biggest barrier to a long and healthy life, but a study published in 2012 found that those sections of the population who sit for three hours or less per day outlive the rest of us by as much as two years. And reducing that a little bit more, to a maximum of two and a half hours, gives you an extra two and a half years on your life.

The problem is how to keep yourself on your feet if you have a desk job. The advice is to do more of your work on your feet: take phone calls standing up, for instance. The key is to take a break from sitting down every 20 to 30 minutes; there are apps which will send you reminders to get up regularly. It will help boost your productivity by keeping you more alert, it can help relieve muscle tension, back and hip ache and it might just help you live longer too.

TIP 37

STOP EATING
★ CRISPS ★

Gary Lineker might be prepared to go to extraordinary lengths for them, if advertising campaigns are to be believed, but the humble potato crisp has to go if you want to maximise your chances of living a long, healthy life.

The first thing weighing against a daily bag of ready salted is the impact on our waistline: eating just a single ounce a day will add two pounds to your weight over the course of a year. But the real dangers lie in more than just the fat and calorie content. Crisps are high in sodium, which can send our blood pressure soaring, trans-fats that push up cholesterol levels and also in a carcinogen called acrylamide, formed by the process of being cooked at high temperature.

Acrylamide occurs in any cooking process that involves high temperature, including toasting bread and home-frying potato chips. To minimise risk, eat lightly toasted bread and pre-boil your potatoes before frying, cooking them only until they are lightly golden.

TIP 38

EAT MORE
WHOLE GRAINS

If you're already a fan of porridge, sandwiches and pasta, you're onto a good thing. Just as long as you have made the switch from processed to whole grain.

We have long been told to work more whole grains into our diet, because of the positive effect they can have on our cholesterol and heart health. But until 2016, no scientific studies had examined exactly what impact a diet rich in whole grains can have on our life expectancy.

A Harvard team looked at the results from a number of studies into whole grains from around the world, collating evidence from more than 780,000 participants, and the results were conclusive. Those of us who routinely eat 70 grams of whole grains a day are as much as 20 per cent less likely to die prematurely; the dietary advice is that we exceed this amount on a daily basis, with starchy wholegrain foods such as wholegrain pasta, bread and rice making up about a third of every meal.

Much of the nutritional value of the grains we eat every day is lost when they are processed; in contrast, whole grains are rich in fibre, iron and B vitamins. Eating 48g a day can see your chances of premature death fall by 15 per cent, so reach for the wholemeal bread, wholewheat pasta, brown rice, oatmeal, quinoa, bulgar and home-popped corn.

TIP 39

START EACH DAY WITH A
STRETCH

If your morning routine involves nothing more healthful than a couple of cups of strong coffee and an invigorating shower, perhaps it's time to incorporate something new. Devotees of yoga have long felt the benefits of early morning stretching, and will tell you that starting your day with a simple five-minute yoga session helps set heart, mind, lymphatic and digestive systems up for the day.

It may also help elongate your life, as morning stretching can help eradicate metabolic products which build up overnight and which speed up the ageing process. So throw open the curtains, or step outside if you can, dosing yourself up on a little vitamin D in the process, and you're ready to start. Begin by stretching it out: reach your arms up to the sky and gently bend to each side, exhaling as you do so. Then try a forward fold, to stretch your full body ahead of the day, and a meditative tree pose. A cat-cow and a downward dog to round off will get your blood pumping and your breathing regulated.

TIP 40

STOP SAYING
'YES'

NOTHING AGES US LIKE STRESS. IN THE PUSH FOR A BETTER CAREER, HAPPIER FAMILY AND BROAD SOCIAL CIRCLES, IT CAN BE ALL TOO EASY TO FIND OURSELVES IN A CYCLE OF SAYING 'YES' TO EVERYTHING THAT'S ASKED OF US: OVERTIME, FAVOURS FOR FRIENDS, WELCOMING VISITORS WE SECRETLY HAVE NOTHING IN COMMON WITH, OR SOCIALISING WITH PEOPLE WHOSE COMPANY WE DON'T ACTUALLY LIKE.

If this sounds all too familiar, it's time to pause and reflect: if saying 'yes' is robbing you of your down-time and keeping your stress levels high, you could be stocking up health problems that might just foreshorten your life. Time to take back a little control and start saying 'no' once in a while.

A sense of control over your life, in which you feel you have the capacity to call at least some of the shots, some of the time, and a meaningful social circle, rather than a vast but unrewarding one, are the building blocks of a stress-busting lifestyle. So next time your head screams 'no', let your mouth do the same.

TIP 41

PRACTISE
SERENITY

We've all had those days where a series of unfortunate events sees us start out anxious and then snowball into meltdown. Your palms are clammy, your forehead's sweaty, you're starting to get palpitations and your breathing's really fast. Anxiety takes over and you're left feeling powerless to its effects.

If this kind of scenario is uncomfortably familiar to you, you will already know that it's doing you no good. In fact, living with this level of anxiety for a sustained period can shorten your life, so it needs to be tackled.

Try nipping the anxiety in the bud: when you feel it begin to mount, close your eyes, concentrate on slowing your breathing down with a few long, slow, deep breaths and then find a little routine that works for you. For some, it's a soothing playlist; for others it's repeating a little mantra in your head: 'You're safe. You're in control. All is well.' Others carry a little bottle of lavender oil or balm and massage it into their pulse points. Try a few techniques, find the one that works best for you and use it as often as you can. Anxiety is a state of mind, but then so is serenity; choose the latter over the former.

KEEP A
★ JOURNAL ★

Life's not always a walk in the park, as much as we would like it to be. Meditation has been proven to help combat the stresses and strains of modern living, reducing anxiety, boosting mental health and keeping us healthy for longer. But if you've tried it and found it's not your bag, perhaps there's another way.

Keeping a journal can be just as cathartic. You don't need to be Samuel Pepys, either: fill it with whatever works for you, whether that's words, pictures, images or memorabilia. What matters is the act of reflection. Taking time to think over what's gone well as well as what's gone badly is an act of meditation in itself, and the act of recording it helps to mentally wrap it up and send it packing. This can be enormously empowering, releasing endorphins, de-stressing and zoning us out for a while, all of which enable us to counter some of the harmful effects of sustained stress on our health and longevity.

Besides, having a record of our worst days to look back on enables us to remember that we've survived tough times before, and came out stronger. Whatever it is, it will pass.

BE A
CURVIER WOMAN

It's true: curvier-hipped women live longer, so if you're pear-shaped, you can afford to celebrate a little. That's according to a team of Danish researchers who carried out a study into the correlation between coronary heart disease and hip circumference. Women who carry a little fat around their hips are protecting their hearts, due to the presence of a vital anti-inflammatory present in significant quantities in hip-fat cells.

Adiponectin prevents a woman's arteries from becoming blocked and the team discovered that its impact is significant in women with a hip size of 40 inches or more: the largest-hipped women had a staggering 86 per cent reduction in the risk of having coronary heart disease, an 87 per cent reduced risk of dying of coronary heart disease, and a 46 per cent reduction in the risk of cardiovascular disease.

Specifically, the study found that women with small, relatively fat-free hips are at greater risk from coronary heart disease because of the comparative absence of adiponectin.

The news isn't quite as encouraging for the larger-hipped guys, however, who don't appear to have a corresponding benefit to their coronary health. And if your hips come with an abdomen of similar girth, your risk of heart disease and diabetes is raised by the impact of abdominal fat cells on insulin levels.

TIP 44

WALK

★ FASTER ★

Getting active and staying active is good for us all, but it isn't just a question of how often and for how long we exercise; it seems that the speed with which we routinely walk is a significant indicator of life expectancy. The results of a study published in an American medical journal in 2011 found that older adults who routinely cover more than three feet per second with their normal walking pace live significantly longer than their slower-paced peers. And fast-paced walking increased a 75-year-old's chances of living for 10 years or more by as much as 91 per cent.

But the results don't suggest that picking up the pace of your walk when you are already in your dotage will help alter your life expectancy: simply that your natural pace is a good indicator of your health and vitality. However, there are plenty of studies which support the benefits of introducing even a small amount of daily activity. While we should all aim for around 150 minutes a week of moderate exercise, walking at your natural pace for as little as 15 minutes daily can have a really positive impact, with over-60s who take a 15-minute daily stroll outliving their less active peers by 22 per cent.

CYCLE
TO WORK

Are you a fully paid-up member of the Men-in-Lycra fan club, or do cyclists give you road-rage? If angry motoring's your thing, perhaps it's time you had a little rethink. In the Netherlands cycling is an art form, with an impressive 37,000 kilometres of Dutch roads carved up for optimal pedal-power. And a study undertaken by Dutch scientists has revealed that there are sound medical reasons why more of us should take their lead: cyclists live longer than the rest of us.

The Dutch findings suggest that vigour, rather than length of time spent on a bike, holds the key. And a Danish study found that among 5,000 already healthy people who cycle regularly, men who pedalled fast outlived the others by more than five years and speedy female cyclists survived their steady-paced peers by 3.9 years. The *International Journal of Sports Medicine* reported in 2011 that another study found that Tour de France cyclists outlive the rest of the population by an average of eight years.

There is a cautionary note to all these great incentives to pedal often and pedal hard. Men in their 50s who are spending more than nine hours a week on their bikes have been found to be five times more likely to be diagnosed with prostate cancer, though the team from University College London are yet to unpick the reasons for the findings. They believe it could simply be an indication that men who cycle in middle age are more likely to seek a diagnosis because they take a closer interest in their health.

TIP 46

TURN OFF
YOUR TELEVISION

EVERYONE KNOWS THAT SPENDING TOO MUCH OF YOUR TIME WATCHING TELEVISION IS BAD FOR YOUR HEALTH, BUT EUROPEANS STILL SPEND AN AVERAGE OF FOUR HOURS A DAY IN FRONT OF THE TELEVISION SET; THE AVERAGE AMERICAN OR AUSTRALIAN WATCHES FOR FIVE HOURS.

Research at Harvard first linked TV watching to obesity more than 25 years ago. The more you watch, the more likely you are to gain weight or become overweight or obese. Television viewing has also been associated with increased aggression, lower academic performance, poor diet and even increased substance use and abuse.

More recent scientific studies have issued a stark warning to those who make the goggle box a major part of their life. A 2010 study found that people who watch television for four or more hours each day are 46 per cent more likely to die from any cause than people who watch less than two hours each day. A 2011 Harvard study associated prolonged viewing with increased risk of Type 2 diabetes, cardiovascular disease and premature death. So if you want to live long and prosper, stop watching science fiction box sets and get off the couch.

TIP 47

★ VOLUNTEER ★

Helping others lead a more fulfilling life helps you live a longer one, according to a review of forty medical studies into the health effects of volunteering carried out by the University of Exeter in 2013. Those who dedicate regular chunks of their down-time to caring for the elderly, or helping at soup kitchens, homeless shelters or food banks can expect to extend their longevity by as much as 22 per cent.

Volunteers who devote at least an hour a month to the service of others over an extended period of time were found across all studies to enjoy a raft of health benefits. Significantly, the incidence of depression was reduced among volunteers. Researchers speculate that a major contributing factor to these findings was the positive impact on loneliness and social isolation volunteers are able to enjoy; loneliness has been widely associated with an increased risk of stroke and heart disease. And socially active people have been found to have a 70 per cent reduction in the risk of dementia, adding extra incentive to get busy volunteering.

Scientists have speculated that volunteers are kept physically active, as well as deriving a deep sense of satisfaction and wellbeing from the act of caring for others, all of which could be contributing to their increased life expectancy.

TIP 48

BE
ECCENTRIC

If you dine with your livestock, bathe during strategy meetings or dye your sheep to brighten up your country pad, you're in good company. The great British eccentric is a national institution. During the two world wars, the great military tactician, Major-General Orde Charles Wingate, was given to greeting foreign diplomats in the nude and latterly abandoned bathing in favour of scrubbing himself down with a toothbrush, which he often did in company. Science now suggests that lifelong kookiness on this scale may actually help us live longer.

In 1995 a psychiatrist from Edinburgh named David Weeks published a book in which he detailed the results of his decade-long study into eccentricity. He found a much-reduced incidence of depression among eccentrics and, interestingly, also discovered that they are visiting the GP twenty times less often than the rest of us.

Eccentricity most commonly goes hand-in-hand with optimism, Weeks found, which in turn keeps the human endocrine system healthy. Less stress, less illness, less time in GP waiting rooms. Non-conformity, it seems, is good for the immune system and adds a few glorious years onto your oddball life.

PLAY MORE
TEST CRICKET

If it's a longer innings in life you're wanting, you could do worse than to spend your days playing as much successful Test cricket as you can manage. A tall order, perhaps, for those of us who don't know our sticky wickets from our cream teas, but it's one way to extend your dotage, according to the results of a study into the longevity of British cricketers, published in the *British Journal of Sports Medicine* in 2008.

The reason for the longevity of our best cricketers appears to come from something more subtle than maintaining a good level of fitness: the longest-living of all cricketers studied were those who had played Test cricket 25 times or more over their careers. Success in the sport at the highest level, then, appears to have kept people in the game of life for longer, by as much as eight years, the survey found. The scientists from the University of St Andrews speculated that the secret might lie in the kudos and personal satisfaction that comes with being at the peak of your sport. This may be powerful enough to combat the effects of stress, keeping the players healthy for longer.

So while not everyone can play Test cricket, it seems that there is much to be gained from reaching the top of your game and staying there.

★ WIN AN OSCAR ★

OLD ACTORS NEVER DIE, AS THE SAYING GOES, THEY JUST LOSE THE PLOT. EXCEPT THAT ACCORDING TO A CANADIAN STUDY, WHILE ACTORS DO EVENTUALLY SHUFFLE OFF THIS MORTAL COIL LIKE THE REST OF US, THEY DO SO A FEW YEARS LATER IF THEY'VE WON AN ACADEMY AWARD.

It has long been recognised that the wealthier you are, the more likely you are to outlive your poorer peers. But in 2001 a team of researchers from the University of Toronto discovered a surprising trend among Oscar nominees. Those who had won the award were outliving the unsuccessful nominees by four years; those who had accumulated two or more Oscars were outliving them by six years. And those nominees who go home empty-handed were living no longer than their unrecognised professional peers.

Unpicking the reasons behind the trend is a complex process: Oscar winners might be paying closer attention to their looks, for example, and therefore also to their health. They may take fewer risks with their health in order to better secure their careers. Success at the highest level may also bring with it the financial capacity to minimise the stresses of everyday life and maximise down-time. Or it may be that standing at the pinnacle of your career simply brings with it a deep sense of wellbeing which is significantly conducive to good health.

Whatever the reasons, when it comes to landing a recurring role in the theatre of life, it seems it's all about the win.

TIP 51

BE A
FIRSTBORN BABY

Firstborn children have long been recognised as more likely to be the most ambitious and the highest achieving of any sibling, as embodied by firstborns such as JK Rowling, Oprah Winfrey, Angela Merkel and anyone who has ever walked on the moon.

But scientific evidence is mounting that firstborns are also healthier and longer-living than their peers. A major US study into longevity using census records discovered that 1.7 times more centenarians had been firstborn siblings; the reason behind the trend is believed to be maternal age at the time of the baby's birth.

Other studies have also found evidence that maternal age significantly impacts on longevity, with those born to women aged 25 or younger being twice as likely to live beyond a century. Firstborns are more likely to be born to a woman in her early 20s than successive siblings.

The data also suggested that firstborn daughters are even more likely to be long-lived than sons and are three times as likely to live to see 100.

GET A
COLONOSCOPY

COLON CANCER (ALSO KNOWN AS COLORECTAL CANCER OR BOWEL CANCER) IS THE SECOND MOST COMMON CAUSE OF CANCER DEATH IN THE UK AFTER LUNG CANCER. A FEW COLON CANCERS HAVE A GENETIC COMPONENT, BUT MOST ARE LINKED TO OLD AGE AND LIFESTYLE (OBESITY, HIGH CONSUMPTION OF FAT, ALCOHOL OR RED MEAT, SMOKING AND A LACK OF PHYSICAL EXERCISE).

Symptoms may include worsening constipation, blood in the stool, a change in bowel movements, loss of appetite, weight loss and fatigue. If you are experiencing some or all of these symptoms, or you are concerned about the health of your lower intestine, your doctor may recommend a colonoscopy.

After being given a sedative and a painkiller, you will lie on your side so the doctor can pump air into your bowel and insert a thin flexible tube called a colonoscope up your backside to look at the colon, to search for ulcers, polyps, tumours, areas of bleeding or inflammation and to collect tiny tissue samples if necessary. All you have to do in preparation is to restrict your food and drink and take medication (under the guidance of your doctor) to clean out the colon so the colonoscope can get a clear view of the intestinal wall. The entire procedure should take less than an hour and it could save your life.

TIP 53

BE AN
AUTUMN BABY

Are you a late-Virgo, a Libra or a Scorpio? If so, good news! All other factors aside, your chances of living to see your hundredth birthday outstrip those with spring or summer star signs.

In a study carried out by scientists from the University of Chicago in 2012, centenarians were found to most commonly have been born in September, October and November. This trend was particularly prevalent in the data from census records of those born before 1890, suggesting that seasonal illnesses in early childhood, in an era of less effective healthcare and medical treatment, are most likely to account for the findings. The precise reasons are as yet unclear, however. Scientists also speculated that women may have been exposed to more seasonal illnesses and had access to less nutritious diets at crucial stages of their pregnancies or while breastfeeding their infants, making babies more robust if born and nursed during certain times of the year.

Whatever the reasons, Leonid Gavrilov and Natalia Gavrilova found that of the 1,600 Americans in the study, people were as much as 40 per cent more likely to live to 100 if they were born between September and November.

TIP 54

★ STAY IN SCHOOL ★

AN EDUCATION IS A GLORIOUS THING, AND SCIENCE
SUGGESTS THAT NOT ONLY DOES IT HELP US TO
RICHER, MORE FULFILLING LIFESTYLES, BUT IT
CAN ALSO HELP US LEAD HEALTHIER
AND LONGER LIVES.

A US study carried out in 2015 found that those Americans who had stayed in school long enough to get their High School diplomas were significantly less likely to die prematurely. In fact, the study estimated that 145,000 US deaths a year could be prevented by remaining in High School until graduation, a figure that compared to the number of deaths avoidable by quitting smoking.

The study looked at death rates in relation to levels of education in the States since 1925 and found that longevity increased at a faster rate over the period studied among those who were more highly educated.

A number of factors are thought to play a part. Better-educated Americans were found to be less likely to smoke and more likely to adopt a lifestyle conducive to the prevention of coronary heart disease. Whether education simply leads us to make healthier choices, or whether it's a less tangible combination of education enabling a less stressful and more fulfilled lifestyle, one thing is clear. Staying in school helps us live longer.

BE A
MILDLY DEPRESSED
WOMAN

Depression is a debilitating and increasingly common illness across all ages, significantly impacting on our quality of life. Worse, sustained depression has been widely associated with early mortality. So when the results of a single scientific study at Duke University in the US in 2002 were found to buck that trend, unsurprisingly it was met with some opposition from the scientific community.

Professor Dan Blazer published his findings in the *American Journal of Geriatric Psychiatry*. Blazer's study had a narrower focus than most other studies into depression and mortality: he was interested only in the effects of mild depression. He found that 10.6 per cent of women in his survey could be diagnosed with mild depression and that these women were on average 60 per cent less likely to die within any three-year period than those without any depression at all.

Mild depression, Blazer speculated, could be a survival mechanism, enabling us to find the resilience to cope with difficult periods of our lives and forcing us to back away from harmful situations and sustained periods of stress.

TIP 56

BECOME A
★ VEGETARIAN ★

The health benefits of a vegetarian diet are undeniable. Vegetarians have a lower incidence of obesity, heart disease, hypertension and Type 2 diabetes, so cutting meat from your diet is a great way to improve your health and longevity, as long as you are careful to find an alternative source to replace the vitamins and nutrients in your diet that you currently get from meat.

A recent study in the journal *JAMA Internal Medicine* examined data from seven clinical studies and 32 other studies from 1900 to 2013 and showed unequivocally that vegetarians have lower blood pressure than meat-eaters. They also tend to eat less saturated fat and cholesterol, leaving their arteries less clogged, than meat-eaters. Consequently, a 2013 study of 44,000 people found that vegetarians are 32 per cent less likely to develop ischemic heart disease.

Vegetarianism also reduces susceptibility to a wide range of cancers, and a recent study from Loma Linda University in California reported that vegans have lower cancer rates than vegetarians. For example, vegan women in the study had 34 per cent lower rates of female-specific cancers such as breast, ovarian and cervical cancer.

However, recent newspaper reports indicate that populations following a vegetarian diet over many generations are more susceptible to cancer, because the DNA becomes altered, making it easier for the body to absorb essential fatty acids from plants, but also increasing production of arachidonic acid, which is linked to inflammatory disease and cancer.

So, curiously enough, switching to a vegetarian diet is great for you as an individual but terrible if all your descendants were to follow your example plus only procreate with vegetarians for a few hundred years. So basically, make the switch by all means, but don't use it as the basis for a new domestic religion.

TIP 57

LIVE A MEANINGFUL LIFE

Do you like what you do? Do you believe you make a difference? Do you have a sense of control over your daily life, or does it too often feel as if life is rushing by, out of your control? According to a study published in *The Lancet* in 2014, the way in which you answer these questions could have a significant impact on how long you live.

The happiest people in a survey carried out by scientists in London were those who measured highly against certain indicators of wellbeing. Over the eight-year period of the study of 9,000 people over the age of 65, 9 per cent of the happiest people died in comparison to the 29 per cent who died in the 'least happy' category. Driving the happiness quotas of those surveyed was a strong sense of purpose: a devotion to a pet or their garden, for instance.

The lesson? Stay busy, make time to do what you love and keep doing it for as long as you can. It might be adding years to your life.

TIP 58

WIN
A NOBEL PRIZE

NELSON MANDELA WAS 95. FRANCIS CRICK WAS 88. ALEXANDER SOLZHENITSYN WAS 89. IF YOU'RE STRUGGLING TO SEE WHAT THEY HAVE IN COMMON BESIDES THEIR DECENT INNINGS, THEY WERE ALL NOBEL PRIZE WINNERS.

In 2007 scientists from the University of Warwick compared the longevity of a variety of Nobel Prize-winning scientists to that of their unsuccessful fellow nominees between the years 1900 and 1950 (details of those nominated are kept under wraps for 50 years). They discovered that the winners outlived the nominees by an average of 1.4 years, longer when winners and nominees from the same countries were compared.

The team considered and factored out the impact the Nobel's cash prize may have had, and discovered that two or more nominations did not have the same impact as a win, leaving them to conclude that the status which comes with success on that level works some kind of magic on our health and wellbeing, which in turn extends our life expectancy.

BE
EMOTIONALLY STABLE

In 2008 the results of a study into the association between personality traits and longevity were published in the journal *Psychosomatic Medicine*. It examined 2,359 participants from the Baltimore Longitudinal Study of Aging, starting in 1958 and concluded: 'In a large sample of generally healthy individuals followed for almost five decades, longevity was associated with being conscientious, emotionally stable, and active.'

Emotional stability is a key personality component for long life (it was found to be the number one indicator of longevity in women) but other scientists have discovered an extra bonus: the older you get, the more emotionally balanced you become. A study led by Laura Carstensen, a psychology professor and director of the Stanford Center on Longevity, has shown that getting older leads to emotional stability. German neuroscientists from University Medical Centre Hamburg-Eppendorf have identified a 'positivity effect': a biased tendency towards emotionally gratifying experiences as we age. In other words, we actively seek out more positive experiences and allow ourselves to be less distracted by negative ones.

Emotionally stable people handle stress well, reducing their risk of dying from stress-related illnesses such as heart disease and cancer. So being emotionally stable helps you live longer, and the older you get, the more emotionally stable you become, helping you to live even longer still.

DONATE
TO CHARITY

DO YOU GET A BIGGER KICK OUT OF WATCHING YOUR DAD UNWRAP HIS MUSICAL CHRISTMAS TIE THAN YOU GET FROM OPENING YOUR OWN GIFTS? IF SO, YOU'RE EXPERIENCING THE PSYCHOLOGICAL PHENOMENON LABELLED 'HELPER'S HIGH'.

Behavioural scientists are increasingly acknowledging the health benefits of generosity. A team of researchers from the National Institute of Health in the US found that when we donate money to charity, the brain churns out endorphins and oxytocin, making us feel invigorated, euphoric and better-connected to the people around us. It also activates the brain's snuggly regions, the bits that tell us we feel good when we're in the company of people we like. In fact giving can help us combat stress, fend off depression and extend our life expectancy, in ways that receiving help doesn't seem to.

There is another reason why scientists believe generosity may be helping the charitable live longer. Those who regularly practise acts of generosity have been found to share a more pronounced sense of gratitude: those who give are more mindful of what they have. Crucially, the grateful have been found to be more likely to exercise and look after their health. Giving to others, in the form of your time or your money, is as good for you as it is for the recipient.

TIP 61

LIVE NEAR
GREEN SPACES

COUNTRY LIVING OR FAST-PACED CITY LIFE? WHICHEVER YOU FAVOUR, A STUDY PUBLISHED IN 2016 SUGGESTS THAT WE SHOULD ALL STRIVE TO SPEND A GREATER PROPORTION OF OUR WEEK IN AN OPEN GREEN SPACE.

The study team looked at data relating to more than 100,000 nurses in the US from 2000 to 2008. They took into account the income and level of education of all participants in the survey and discovered that women are 34 per cent less likely to die from respiratory illness and 13 per cent less likely to die of cancer if they live in green areas, compared to paved and concreted environments.

Lifestyles afforded by access to open green space could account for much of the findings: green spaces invite exercise. However, green spaces could also counteract the more harmful effects of pollution and boost mental health, with consistently lower levels of depression, anxiety and stress exhibited by women living near parks or open countryside.

HAVE
LOTS OF FRIENDS
IN YOUR DOTAGE

'One loyal friend is worth ten thousand relatives', or so claimed the Ancient Greek philosopher Euripides, back in the 5th century BC. Recent research into friendship and longevity suggests that Euripides knew what he was talking about.

If, like him, you love your family but regard your friends as the family you get to choose, you could be in for a long and happy life. That's according to a study into longevity carried out in Australia, which found that no matter how regularly a person is in touch with their relatives in old age, it's the number of friends you keep and how frequently you socialise with them that keeps you alive and kicking the longest.

Across all social demographics, those with the most active and fulfilling social networks were found to be 22 per cent less likely to die over the decade of the study than those with the smallest social circles. The trend held fast even after significant personal trauma, such as the death of a spouse. Other studies have gone so far as to say that a marked sparsity of friendship in our latter years can be as detrimental to our health as smoking 15 cigarettes a day. Friends, the scientists behind the study believe, encourage us to take better care of ourselves, to remain more active in later years and help combat debilitating mental health issues such as depression and anxiety.

RETIRE

★ LATER ★

If you plan on giving up the daily grind as early as possible and retiring to fill long, lazy days with sun, sand and sudoku, you could be inadvertently shortening your lifespan. According to a 2016 study, those who remain in work for even one year past standard retirement age, to retire at 66, could be reducing their risk of premature death by as much as 11 per cent. Clocking on every day until their 70th birthday made participants 44 per cent less likely to die over the 18 years of the survey.

Staying in work not only keeps us more active and more financially secure for longer, but it has a significant impact on our mental health and sense of wellbeing, increasing our social interactions and sense of purpose. Even those in the survey who were of poor health were found to be 9 per cent more likely to outlive their poorly peers if they remained in work for a year longer.

The results give even more incentive to those of us in mid-life to take the best care of our health that we can: poor health is the biggest cause of early retirement in the UK.

HAVE
LOTS OF FRIENDS
IN YOUR TWENTIES

When it comes to friendship, most of us would agree that quality trumps quantity. Except that a 30-year-long psychological survey into the impact of friendship on longevity in different stages of our lives, published in 2015, suggests that there may be crucial exceptions to this adage.

From the age of 30 it is true that a few close, reliable friends make all the difference. However those people surveyed who had the largest social circles in their 20s were found to have significantly fewer mental health issues and a markedly better sense of wellbeing by the age of 50 – both of which are strong indicators of longevity.

The scientists behind the study suggest that casting your net wide in your 20s gives you the greatest opportunity to meet people with whom you are likely to be able to sustain an emotionally close and rewarding friendship.

So, while you're young, travel, experience new situations and meet as many new people as you can. Not only will you have a ball doing so, but you'll be giving yourself the best chance of a long and happy life.

TRAVEL
BY TRAIN

IF YOU'RE A FERROEQUINOLOGIST, YOU MAY ALREADY BE
ON YOUR WAY TO MAXIMISING YOUR CHANCES OF LIVING
TO A RIPE OLD AGE. AND IF YOU'RE A FAN OF THE RAILWAY,
YOU HAVE A BETTER CHANCE OF KNOWING WHAT
A 'FERROEQUINOLOGIST' IS.

If you regularly opt to travel by rail rather than by road you are statistically improving the odds of avoiding an early death. This is because of all modern means of transport, there are fewest rail-related deaths. Your risk of dying in a motor vehicle accident before the age of 75 years is an alarming 1 in 413; compare that to death by train travel which is 1 in 131,313. Suddenly 'standing room only' on the 8:15, but arriving alive and intact, starts to look a lot more appealing than the convenience, guaranteed seat but possible early death afforded by driving yourself.

If you find you come to love seeing the world from the inside of a railway carriage, you can extend your longevity even more by travelling further afield: holidays, according to an Australian study, not only make us feel more rejuvenated, they can make significant contributions to our health, cutting through the effects of stress and anxiety to help us live longer.

CUT YOUR
★ CALORIES ★

It doesn't take much imagination to figure out what members of the Calorific Restriction Optimal Nutrition Society put on their plates.
Yep, you guessed it: tiny portions. But they seem to be staying younger and living longer as a consequence.

Eighteen society members, who had been eating between 1,100 and 1,950 calories daily, were compared to a matched group whose intake was higher: between 1,975 and 3,550 calories. The group with the lower calorie consumption scored much better in terms of cholesterol, blood pressure and insulin levels – the three key risk factors of heart disease and diabetes.

Their 'bad' cholesterol (LDL) was in the lowest 10 per cent of people in their age group, and their 'good' cholesterol (HDL) was in the highest 15 per cent. Their level of triglycerides (fats that contribute to hardening of the arteries) were lower than 95 per cent of Americans half their age.
A similar result was observed during the Biosphere Two experiments in the early 1990s, where the participants ended up on a calorie-restriction (C-R) diet when supplies ran low. Their blood pressure fell and their cholesterol dropped on average by forty points. The US government has caught on to the health potential of the C-R diet and is spending 20 million dollars on the first large-scale human trials.

'Experiments in mice have been going on for several decades, and have certainly shown that caloric restriction will extend lifespan,' says Dr Evan Hadley of the National Institute of Health.

TIP 67

EAT MORE
SEEDS

You probably haven't heard of a body called the Global Burden of Disease; it isn't often in the news. It's a division of the World Health Organization and is devoted to the careful analysis and measurement of illness and disease across the world, looking at the impact of disease on disability and premature death.

As part of its ongoing work, the GBD has issued a checklist of foods we aren't getting enough of in rank order of the damage to health caused by their absence from our diet. High on the list is too little fresh fruit, but following closely behind is a diet poor in seeds and nuts.

So why not start tossing a handful of seeds onto your morning muesli or your daily salad? Try hemp, which boosts brain function; pumpkin, for anxiety-reduction and a better night's sleep; sunflower, high in immunity-boosting folates; and antioxidant-rich sesame seeds.

TIP 68

EAT
AN APPLE A DAY

This is one our grandmothers knew before us, and that their grandmothers knew before them: *an apple a day keeps the doctor away*. Science, it seems, is finally catching on to the idea.

Longevity studies using fruit flies have discovered that not only does a diet rich in apples keep the fruit fly alive for longer – up to 10 per cent longer – but a substance found in apples enables the fly to remain active for longer too. In other studies, women who regularly eat apples have been found to have a 13 to 22 per cent reduced chance of heart disease than their apple-shy peers.

The secret lies in the apple's natural supply of antioxidants, called polyphenols, which fight the presence of ageing free-radicals in the body. In addition flavonoids, present in high quantities in apple skin, work on our arteries and help prevent cell damage.

In the quest for the apple which most extends life, a British team triumphed in 2008 when they discovered that an ancient, bitter and pink-fleshed variety of British hawthorn apple contained high levels of a compound named epicatechin. The apple, redeveloped as a variety named Evesse, was found to have a marked effect on arterial health, with regular consumption prompting a 63 per cent greater likelihood of living beyond your 82nd birthday.

TIP 69

BE A SEVENTH-DAY ADVENTIST

When longevity researchers in the US noticed that in one Californian town residents were bucking the national trend and living on average 10 years longer than their fellow Americans, naturally they wanted to find out why. The answer was apparently very simple: the town of Loma Linda is home to a high concentration of Seventh-day Adventists. A vegetarian diet, high in raw foods, and an absence of both tobacco and alcohol were immediately evident. But researchers discovered that didn't fully account for this community's long-living tendencies.

Two other elements of their religious beliefs and practices, however, were found to be of particular significance. Seventh-day Adventists, as a community, are not only watching what they eat, but they're also a hard-working and active bunch. And because they place such high emphasis on keeping strong social bonds, they are all setting each other the best possible examples, encouraging each other in deed as well as word to stay active.

There's one final element to the community's routine which researchers realised plays a significant part. From sun-down every Friday evening, Seventh-day Adventists power down, respecting their day of rest and spending it with friends and family, and in meditative prayer and reflection. They chill, for 24 hours every week. Without fail. Diet, exercise, stress-management: it's no wonder there are more centenarians living in Loma Linda than anywhere else in the US.

★ BE A SHORT PERSON ★

TALL MEN EARN MORE MONEY THAN SHORT MEN AND
RICH PEOPLE LIVE LONGER THAN POOR PEOPLE, SO YOU
WOULD EXPECT TALL MEN TO LIVE LONGER THAN SHORT
MEN. IN FACT THE OPPOSITE IS TRUE: TALL MEN HAVE
A HIGHER INCIDENCE OF CANCER AND
CARDIAC-RELATED DEATHS.

Tall women fare no better. A recent study led by Geoffrey Kabat of the Albert Einstein College of Medicine showed that each additional four inches of height increases the risk of all types of cancer by 13 per cent among post-menopausal women.

In European countries there is a correlation between average height and the rate of death from heart disease. For example, Swedes and Norwegians have an average height of 5 feet 10 inches and have more than twice as many cardiac deaths per 100,000 than the Spanish and Portuguese, who average 5 feet 5 inches in height. A 1992 study of 1,700 men found that those who were shorter than 5 feet 9 inches averaged 71 years at death, versus 64 years for those taller than 6 feet 4 inches. Most centenarians worldwide are 5 feet 5 inches or below.

In nearly every species in the animal kingdom, the smaller individuals live longer. There are several explanations for this. Tall people have more cells, with a corresponding increased risk of some of them mutating and becoming cancerous. The lungs and circulatory system have to work harder in a taller person relative to the body's needs, so blood pressure is higher. There is also an increased risk of blood clots, possibly related to the length and weight of the columns of blood in the body of a taller person. Tall people also suffer more illness, even when gender is eliminated as a variable.

So if you're a short person, congratulations – but don't get complacent. This doesn't mean you can thrash your body harder than your lofty contemporaries. Studies reveal that unhealthy short people die sooner than unhealthy tall people, so always complement your lack of height with proper nutrition and a healthy lifestyle to maximise those benefits.

TIP 71

★ EAT ISOTOPES ★

Ten years ago, Oxford-based researcher Mikhail Shchepinov caused a brief stir in the scientific community by publishing research which, he claimed, had the potential to slow down the ageing process and extend human life by up to ten years. The principle was simple: the Isotope Effect. The presence of heavy isotopes in a molecule slows down its chemical reactions, which is a good thing if those reactions involve the oxidative damage that causes the degeneration of DNA and amino acids within the body. Shchepinov proposed the replacement of key biological molecules within the human body with more resilient isotopes (naturally occurring atomic variations of chemical elements) to make them less susceptible to ageing.

In 'Meat and two neutrons – the key to a longer life', the Society of Chemical Industry explained in 2007 that 'scientists have shown for the first time that food enriched with natural isotopes builds bodily components that are more resistant to the processes of ageing'. The only problem was that the principle has only been tested on nematode worms, albeit with a promising increased lifespan of ten per cent.

Shchepinov's critics believe that it would be very difficult to deliver these isotopes to specific sites in the human body, and if they got into general circulation in the body they could quickly prove fatal. Heavy water (deuterium oxide, or D_2O – isotope of hydrogen with an atomic mass of 2 instead of 1) is a strong candidate for this process, but its production is expensive and energy intensive (involving the repeated electrolysis or fractional distillation of water), although you'd have to drink several litres (several thousand pounds' worth) to reach toxic levels. But

Shchepinov doesn't advocate glugging heavy water; he is more interested in delivering the isotopes at one step removed – via what he called 'iFoods', for example, chicken from birds that have been fed with D_2O as well as H_2O so the meat proteins already have protective qualities (stronger covalent bonds, making them more resistant to oxidation caused by free radicals).

The idea is a long way from becoming an anti-ageing elixir, but it has been endorsed by one of the leading pioneers in ageing research, the Cambridge-based chief science officer of the Methuselah Foundation, Dr Aubrey de Grey, so it isn't completely dead in the heavy water and may yet irrigate more fertile minds in the near future.

TIP 72

CHECK YOUR
★ BOWELS ★

In recent years, there has been a subtle shift in longevity studies; science is not simply interested in living longer, but in living well for longer. To this end, researchers are concentrating on some of the primary causes of frailty in old age, specifically looking at the inflammation which contributes to that frailty. And they've found that the source of this inflammation is not necessarily where you might expect it.

The digestive system should be home to a healthy balance of microbial life, some of which may have a much greater impact than previously thought on our health and vitality in old age. One study examined the stool samples of sets of twins, finding higher levels of good bodily flora, such as *Faecalibacterium prausnitzii*, in the healthier twin, and higher levels of unhelpful bacteria, such as *Eubacterium dolichum*, in the less healthy twin.

Bowel health, then, could be one of the best indicators of our chances of living to ripe and active old age. In any case, we should all become better acquainted with our poo: spotting changes, in colour or consistency, is vital in the early detection of bowel cancer. Making sensible, long-term changes to your diet, particularly increasing your intake of vegetables, will help create a healthy gut and healthy stools.

★ DRINK GREEN TEA ★

STEP AWAY FROM YOUR ORANGE JUICE AND BREW
YOURSELF A STEAMING CUP OF GREEN TEA, THE MANY
BENEFITS OF WHICH INCLUDE PROTECTION AGAINST
STROKE, COGNITIVE IMPAIRMENT IN OLD AGE,
LIVER DISEASE, HEART DISEASE, JOINT MOBILITY,
DIABETES AND CANCER.

Green tea contains more than 200 complex bioactive compounds, but its major super-ingredient is a substance called Epigallocatechin-3-gallate (also known as EGCG) which has been found to be over 100 times more effective in neutralising free radicals than vitamin C and 25 times more effective than vitamin E.

A large study of women found that those who drank at least five cups of green tea a day had a 42 per cent lower risk of death by stroke than those who drank less than one cup a day; another study found that drinking just two cups a day can halve your risk of cognitive impairment in old age. A meta study of more than 850,000 people found that drinking three cups a day lowers the risk of heart disease by 27 per cent, heart attack by 26 per cent and stroke by 18 per cent.

When cells divide, the telomeres – the repetitive nucleotide sequences at the end of the DNA strands – shorten microscopically. Telomeres have been compared to the cap on the end of a shoelace, which prevents it from unravelling; eventually, however, they become so short that they cannot divide any further, which is why our body tissue and organs deteriorate as we get older. The three American scientists who discovered this mechanism and its role in ageing were awarded the Nobel Prize in 2009. However, green tea has been observed to slow ageing at this genetic level. Drinking three cups each day can give you telomeres the length of someone five years younger.

Finally, green tea laughs in the face of cancer. A 13-year Japanese study found that drinking ten cups a day reduced the risk of cancer by up to 41 per cent, and the effect was more pronounced in women than men.

TIP 74

★ HAVE THIN FRIENDS ★

A study published in the *New England Journal of Medicine* in 2007 revealed that we are 57 per cent more likely to be obese if the three people we regard as our closest friends are also obese.

The study used data initially collated by medics looking into coronary heart disease, by monitoring more than 12,000 people for 32 years. A team of medical sociologists realised that the study contained data on every participant's close family members as well as the people they had named as their closest friends. By reconfiguring the data they were able to study the impact obesity has on a close social group. To the shock of the medical community, they discovered that if a person gained weight, their closest friends were significantly more likely to do the same. Similar results were found for weight loss among social circles, although over the 32 years of the study, weight gain was the norm, leading the researchers to describe obesity as virus-like, spreading from person to person.

The same results were not true for the comparative weight losses and gains among family members, neighbours or colleagues, leading the study to conclude that one way to ensure we don't become obese is to hang out with thin friends.

TIP 75

BE A

BREAST-FED BABY

It has long been known that breast is best when it comes to giving your newborn the best start in life; breast milk is rich in antibodies which give your baby the strongest immunity from day one. Breast-fed babies are less prone to chest and ear infections, as well as statistically less likely to fall victim to Sudden Infant Death Syndrome. But the long-term benefits of breast-feeding are only now being understood.

Several major scientific studies have found that babies who are exclusively breast-fed for the first six months of their lives are 20 per cent less likely to become significantly overweight or obese in childhood and adolescence, the benefits of which continue into adulthood. Furthermore, there is also a significantly lower incidence of childhood diabetes among these children.

Another study was undertaken across all socio-economic groups in Brazil, following 6,000 babies from birth to the age of 30. At the end of the period, researchers discovered that regardless of all other factors, breast-fed babies have higher IQs, are more highly educated and fall into higher income brackets than their bottle-fed contemporaries. And brighter, better-educated and higher-earning individuals live healthier lifestyles and live longer.

TIP 76

BE
LAZY

BACK IN 2012, BRITAIN'S OLDEST LIVING MAN TURNED 112 YEARS OLD AND WHEN ASKED THE SECRET TO HIS LONGEVITY, HE ANSWERED SIMPLY 'IDLENESS'. THE IDEA THAT WE HAVE A FINITE POT OF 'LIFE ENERGY' THAT WILL BE MORE QUICKLY EXPENDED BY A LIFE LIVED FAST AND HECTIC MAY SEEM LACKING IN SCIENTIFIC CLOUT, BUT IT BEARS CLOSER SCRUTINY.

The fast pace of modern living sees more of us spending longer hours at the office, larger chunks of our time battling the daily commute and extending our day later and later into the hours of darkness, with all the subsequent ill-effects of sleep deprivation, stress and anxiety. In contrast, a 2007 study carried out in Greece found that those who built a daily siesta into their routine were a significant 37 per cent less likely to die from coronary events. And a Swedish study took this research further, finding that those who embrace gentle pursuits – reading, painting, a spot of light pottering in the garden – are living on average 15 to 20 years longer than those of us filling frantic hours in fast living. Other studies suggest that a life spent in greater degrees of idleness produces fewer free radicals, the oxygen molecules thought to speed the ageing process.

HAVE A
HIGHER IQ

Several leading medical studies in recent years have concluded that people with a higher IQ are more likely to be longer-living. One study suggested that the higher a child scores in intelligence tests at the age of 11, the more likely they are to live to age 76 and beyond. The jury is out, however, as to the causes of the link between intelligence and longevity.

There are strong environmental factors which could be contributing to the statistics: the more intelligent you are, the more likely you are to make healthy choices over diet and lifestyle, for instance. But evidence is growing that this accounts for only a small part of the reason why 'smarts' are outliving those of more average brain-power.

Studies into fraternal and identical twins in several parts of the world have discovered that even among identical twins, the more intelligent of the pair is more likely to outlive the other. This is particularly the case with fraternal twins, however, leading scientists to theorise that the answer lies in their genetic make-up, and in particular, in the precise make-up of their anti-inflammatory genetic inheritance, since the ageing process is increasingly understood to be significantly affected by inflammation.

QUIT SMOKING

Anyone who smokes already knows that smoking lowers life expectancy and that those who have never smoked can expect to live more than ten years longer on average than those who do. Those who have never smoked are twice as likely to still be around to celebrate their 80th birthday. Plenty of reasons not to take up the habit, then. Globally, if smoking continues at current levels, it's likely to prematurely kill around a billion of us during the 21st century.

For those who do indulge, however, there's some heavy-weight science to persuade you to quit. For those smokers yet to turn 40, the news for you is really good. A study carried out at the University of Toronto in 2013 found that quitting before your 40th birthday takes your life expectancy almost back to where it would have been had you never smoked at all. The likelihood of premature death for those who quit smoking before the onset of middle age is slashed by 90 per cent, in fact. And the earlier you quit, the less your former habit impacts on your longevity.

But the science supports the adage that it's never too late: quitting at any age is statistically proven to significantly extend your life expectancy.

BE A LITTLE
OVERWEIGHT

It's hardly an avoidable message in modern living: sort out your waistline, we are told, and maximise your health. The medical community would like us all to eat more fruit and veg, eat less of everything else, get a little bit more active and reduce our impact on the weighing scales. But some scientists are challenging the idea that skinnies live longer.

Certainly, obesity is likely to shave years off your life expectancy and a Body Mass Index in excess of 35 is a strong indicator for premature mortality. But hidden in the small print of studies into the correlation between weight and mortality rates is a finding that is often overlooked by the media. Remarkably, those who fall into the 'overweight' category, that is, with a BMI between 25 and 30, are actually *outliving* everyone else; not just the obese, but also those with 'normal' BMIs. This hasn't just been the conclusion of a single study: a recent German meta-analysis of all studies into obesity and excess weight found that the overweight among us really are living the longest.

A German professor named Achim Peters has found that those who eat more when stressed equip their brains with the capacity to deal with stress in a less damaging way, when compared to those who stop eating under pressure. Peters says that in a world in which we all develop our own survival strategies, there is no such thing as an 'ideal weight', and that instead, we should focus more on the healthiest methods of coping with stress in our lives.

TIP 80

DRINK
★ COFFEE ★

Love your coffee? Hate the thought of having to start the day without it, no matter what the doctor orders? Well, you may be in luck. Since the 1970s, the verdict over the relationship between coffee and coronary health has been a source of almost constant debate. And the picture looked grimmer still in 1991, when the World Health Organization labelled coffee a possible carcinogen.

But the latest evidence, published in *The Lancet* in 2016, not only clears coffee as a cancer risk, but states that some significant studies point to coffee as a potential cancer-preventative, particularly of liver and endometrial cancers. Furthermore, coffee consumption has been linked with a decreased risk of cardiovascular disease and diabetes, and with longevity in general.

One word of caution though: for those of you who like your drinks piping hot, there is mounting evidence that liquids hotter than around 65 degrees Celsius are tumour-promoting and as such, if consumed regularly, are carcinogenic, whether it's coffee, tea or even plain hot water. So enjoy your coffee, but leave it to cool to around 60 degrees first.

TIP 81

★ FIND GOD ★

If you were to look no further than the Old Testament for a correlation between longevity and belief in God, the evidence would be emphatic: it faithfully records that Noah was 600 years old when he built the Ark and after the flood he enjoyed an additional 350 years of not being dead. Methuselah, the hoary old patriarch and the archetype for unfeasibly extended existence, was 969 when he finally bought the farm.

Science reveals a more nuanced story. Several studies have shown that in developed countries like the US where religious people form the majority, being religious is linked to longer life; however, in secular developed countries like Sweden, where being religious is atypical, it confers no additional health benefits. The most plausible explanation for this is that being active in the local community is good for you and extends your life: in the US,

community activities are often centred around the church, so an atheist would be less likely to become involved, while in Sweden, community involvement is high, so a secular individual would be more likely to participate and feel welcome.

But what about underdeveloped countries? Well, here the link between religion and low mortality is undeniable. The most religious societies in the world tend to be underdeveloped countries, where poverty and disease are high and life expectancy is low. Clearly, in these circumstances religion is no magic bullet, but it does provide vital comfort and psychological strength for those who have to cope with the uncertainties of daily life.

So, if you want to extend your life by being religious, it's only going to prove beneficial if you live in an affluent developed country where religious folk outnumber the infidels.

TIP 82

BE A
POLYGAMOUS
MAN

IF YOU'RE OPEN TO THE VIEW THAT THERE'S MORE THAN ONE MRS RIGHT FOR YOU IN THE WORLD, AND YOU'D LIKE TO LIVE A LONG LIFE, YOU COULD DO BETTER THAN TO LIVE AMONG THE WORLD'S POLYGAMOUS PEOPLES.

A study undertaken at the University of Sheffield in 2008 suggested that men who live in cultures where polygamy is practised, and who have more than one wife, are living on average 12 per cent longer than the rest of us. The study speculated that fathering children with second wives at an older age may encourage the polygamous man to remain active for longer, in order to help raise and feed his children. Equally, evolution may have played a subtle long-game here, selecting the longest-living males from the gene pool in those parts of the world where polygamous men have been called upon to reproduce into and beyond middle age.

Or perhaps the men who take multiple wives are living longer simply because they have younger, more active women on hand to support, nurture and care for them, enabling them to outlive their lonelier, widowed, monogamous peers in other regions of the world. Certainly, the study makes sense when taken in the context of other findings into the longevity of bachelors in comparison with their longer-lived monogamous peers.

TIP 83

EAT

★ RED ★

A HEALTHY DIET IS ONE RICH IN A WIDE VARIETY OF FRUIT AND VEGETABLES; THIS WE ALL KNOW. THE SIMPLEST WAY OF ENSURING WE GET PLENTY OF NUTRITIOUS VARIETY IN OUR DIETS IS TO 'EAT A RAINBOW', SELECTING NATURAL, COLOURFUL FOODS. BUT SELECTING RED FRUIT AND VEG IS PARTICULARLY BENEFICIAL IN BUILDING THE HEALTH AND VITALITY NEEDED TO ENSURE LONGEVITY.

Red foods are rich in powerful antioxidants, particularly lycopene and anthocyanins, which are the body's natural defence against heart disease, cancers and macular degeneration that impacts on our eyesight as we age.

Try tossing some red peppers, beetroot, pomegranate and tomatoes into your salads, for a healthy blend of antioxidants that can help protect against prostate and breast cancer and prevent the build-up of plaque that clogs our arteries. Or spice up your supper with a red hot chilli pepper, proven to increase your metabolic rate and keep you feeling fuller for longer.

Fill your fruit bowl with cherries, rich in potassium, to keep blood pressure low, watermelon to help protect against stroke, and pink grapefruit which can help lower cholesterol (but check with your GP if you're on any medication, as grapefruit can interfere with some medicines). Try stuffing your poultry with cranberries, which help fight cancer cells and protect against stomach ulcers.

TIP 84

LEARN A LANGUAGE

Do you *spreche Deutsch* like a native, or is ordering a frankfurter about your limit? If you've found yourself wondering whether you have what it takes to be a linguist, it's never too late to find out and you might just be extending your life expectancy in the process.

In 2014 a team of researchers from the University of Pennsylvania undertook a study into the effects of a sustained period of learning a new skill, particularly a new language. They found that those who persevered with learning Chinese vocabulary as beginners over a 6-week period, and who had made the most progress by the end of that time, had actually forged new connections between the different nodes in their brains. Learning a new language had physically altered their brain, making it better connected.

This has significant implications for longevity: even in old age, learning a new language helps us age gracefully, strengthening the brain and improving its functions, and crucially, helping to fend off dementia.

TIP 85

JOIN
THE CLERGY

Perhaps Hamlet wasn't so crazy to advise the woman he loved, 'Get thee to a nunnery'. It seems that priests, monks and nuns are outliving us all, and by a significant amount. According to a study of mortality rates carried out in 2002, those of us who have taken up holy orders, to live out life in a monastery, convent or in the priesthood, have among the lowest mortality rates of any occupation on the planet. In the case of Benedictine monks, the mortality rate is almost half that of the comparable civilian population. And at a convent in Italy where nuns take a vow of silence, there was no age-related rise in blood pressure normally seen in women post middle-age; in fact over a 30-year study, the sisters' blood pressures remained remarkably stable.

Diet was initially believed to be the primary reason for the low incidence of disease and mortality, but vast numbers of those in Holy Orders live, work and eat in the wider community. A life of quiet contemplation, with low stress levels and a tradition of not dwelling on concerns about ill-health, is believed to be the most likely factor, and one from which we can all learn.

And if the religious life isn't for you, perhaps you might consider taking up the occupation with the next lowest mortality rate: accountancy.

TIP 86

BECOME
A FIREFIGHTER

A life lived staring death in the face on a daily basis may not strike you as the best way to ensure a long and healthy innings, but in fact a US survey into the nation's safest jobs found that firefighters are outliving the average American, exceeding the typical life expectancy of 79 years. The truth is that where police officers and firefighters survive until retirement, rather than dying on the job, their active, healthy lifestyle and perhaps also the sense of wellbeing that comes from a life lived in the service of others, makes them among the longest living of all of us from that age on.

And as for the years prior to retirement, on-the-job mortality levels are not as great for the firefighter as they are for example in the case of fishermen, loggers or construction workers, all of whom have to continue working in their dangerous jobs beyond the point at which most firefighters retire at 57.

SMILE
FOR THE
CAMERA

WHAT DOES YOUR FACE DO WHEN A CAMERA IS POINTED AT IT? ARE YOU A NATURAL BEAMER, OR IS GURNING MORE YOUR STYLE? IT'S AN IMPORTANT QUESTION IF A LONG LIFE IS HIGH ON YOUR WISH LIST.

A research team in the US studied a number of photographs of former professional baseball players, an athletic cohort already known for their longevity. What the scientists were looking for was the breadth of each player's smile. Astonishingly, they found that those players with the broadest smiles in photographs were also the longest living.

The secret, the team believe, is in how happy you feel, as a big, broad smile is a sure sign of deep-seated happiness. The happier you feel, the healthier you are likely to be and the longer you are likely to live. So treat yourself to your favourite comedy, a long walk outdoors, preferably somewhere green, and a hearty dose of omega-3-rich foods to keep your happy-hormones naturally high.

HAVE THE
RIGHT NAME

Our ancestors believed you could do a lot for a child by giving it an inspirational name. Call your daughter 'Constance' and she was more likely to remain loyal and faithful. A son named 'Björn' would live up to his name in strength and courage (it means bear in Swedish). These days, we generally choose names because we like the way they sound or because they are meaningful in some other way, not because they are reminiscent of personality traits at the top of our parental wish list.

However, prospective parents hoping for a long and happy life for their children may want to consider a research paper published in the *Journal of Psychosomatic Research* in 1999, entitled 'The Theory of Deadly Initials'. The team behind the study found that over a lifetime, those individuals whose full name lends them initials with negative connotations (David Ian Edwards, D.I.E., for instance; or Peter Ian Green, P.I.G.) suffer more stress and low self-esteem, contributing to a shorter life expectancy, when compared to those with positive initials (Adrian Charles Edwards, A.C.E.; or Vincent Ian Philips, V.I.P.), who on average outlive their less fortune peers by as much as 4.48 years.

COMPLAIN
MORE

ARE YOU AN ETERNALLY AGREEABLE SORT? NOT GIVEN TO ROCKING THE BOAT OR GIVING VOICE TO YOUR OBJECTIONS, EVEN IF YOU ARE FAIRLY SURE YOUR OBJECTIONS ARE VALID? DO YOU BITE YOUR LIP, COUNT TO TEN AND SUCK IT UP IN ORDER TO KEEP THE PEACE? IF YOU DO, YOU NEED TO CUT IT OUT.

New research shows that the act of complaining is good for us. It can boost self-esteem, by giving a sense of control over the way in which we are perceived (complaining about a sub-standard wine, for instance, gives us a sense that we have let others know about our discerning good taste). It enables us to seek and receive support from those close to us. And it relieves stress and reduces anxiety, both of which will give your immune system a boost. Other studies have found that cancer patients who complain about their illness outlive their fellow sufferers who take their condition on the chin.

And all of that might be helping you live longer, by as much as two years, according to some scientific studies.

TIP 90

★ FLOSS ★

RECENT RESEARCH FROM THE AMERICAN ACADEMY OF PERIODONTOLOGY FOUND THAT MORE THAN A THIRD OF PEOPLE SURVEYED WOULD RATHER CLEAN A TOILET THAN FLOSS. CLEARLY, IF YOU FIND FLOSSING BORING, UNCOMFORTABLE AND FRUSTRATING, YOU'RE NOT ALONE. BUT HOW ABOUT THIS FOR AN INCENTIVE: CLEANING A TOILET DOES NOT IMPROVE LONGEVITY, BUT REGULAR FLOSSING CAN ADD MORE THAN SIX YEARS TO YOUR LIFE.

There is a well-established link between dental health and longevity. People with diseases such as gingivitis and periodontitis have a mortality rate up to 46 per cent higher than those who don't. The bacteria that cause these dental diseases damage the rest of your body in two ways. First, when the bacteria gets into the blood stream it forms plaque on the walls of your arteries (like the plaque that the dental hygienist scrapes off your teeth every six months), making them narrower and more prone to becoming blocked, raising blood pressure and increasing the risk of heart attack and stroke. Secondly, the bacteria causes inflammation (which is your body's immune response) which also narrows the arteries with the same potentially disastrous consequences. Five minutes of discomfort in front of the bathroom mirror each morning suddenly became less of a chore.

★ CURSE ★
MORE

We are naturally wired to do whatever the body needs us to do whenever it's under threat or in pain. When calm and relaxed, most of what we say and how we say it is controlled by the left brain; when we're under pressure, however, the more emotional right side is more likely to take control of what comes out of our mouths.

And a team of psychologists at Keele University found that if in the face of sudden pain, what comes out of your mouth wouldn't get broadcast before the watershed, you are actually doing yourself an enormous favour. Our pain threshold, and therefore our ability to deal with sudden stress and trauma, is significantly increased when we curse about it.

The team haven't quite figured out why cursing helps, but speculate that perhaps it's something about overcoming the feebleness of simply feeling the pain, while the machismo of swearing about it might be activating our brain's capacity to handle the situation a little longer.

GOSSIP MORE

Seriously, go ahead. I won't tell a soul.

If you are the first to dive into a piece of juicy gossip, you will already know it feels good. If, however, you pride yourself on exercising restraint and quietly sit in judgement on anyone who doesn't, it might be time to think again.

Dishing the dirt with your mates is scientifically proven to extend your life expectancy. In a group of women who took part in a study at the University of Michigan, those asked to discuss personal details about each other, rather than the details of an academic paper, were found to have raised levels of the happy hormone, progesterone, known to combat the ill-effects of stress in women.

Gossip is a quick way of cementing social bonds, and the act of maintaining a strong connection with your social circle is known to boost mental health and increase longevity. Conversely, keeping your mind focused on your work to the exclusion of what's going on at the office water cooler sees your progesterone levels drop.

So next time you feel the pressure mounting, a catch-up with the gang might be just what the doctor ordered.

JOIN A
★ CHOIR ★

Does the sound of music make you feel alive? Are you fond of belting out a power ballad in the shower and singing at the top of your lungs along to the car radio? If so, according to a team from the University of London, you're giving your heart and soul a pretty good workout, enabling feel-good endorphins to flood your system as well as exercising your heart and lungs and stretching back and abdominal muscles.

Anyone already fully paid up to the joys of singing through traffic jams will know all too well that it's always better in company. And now there's science to back that up. A research study undertaken at the National Endowment for the Arts at George Washington University in the US found that when people regularly sing in company, for example by

joining a choir, amazing things happen to their health. Choir members suffer lower rates of depression and make fewer visits to their doctor, for instance.

The stress-busting euphoria of singing along with others releases oxytocin, a powerful hormone that counters the worst effects of anxiety and depression, boosts concentration and increases your productivity. What's more, there's no better way to feel socially connected, with one Swedish study finding that members of choirs can become so closely connected through the act of singing together that their heartbeats synch-up.

What a truly harmonious way to boost your health, your happiness and your longevity.

TIP 94

CLEAN THE HOUSE MORE

DO YOU SPEND HOURS EVERY WEEK ON YOUR KNEES SCRUBBING THE FLOOR? LOVE IT OR LOATHE IT, THERE'S NOW AN ADDED INCENTIVE TO GET BUSY WITH YOUR MOP AND BUCKET: PEOPLE WHO SPEND AN EYE-WATERING 17 HOURS A WEEK OR MORE CLEANING THEIR HOUSES ARE LIKELY TO OUTLIVE THE SLOBS AMONG US.

According to a survey of 200,000 women from nine European countries, those women who spend around two and a half hours each day cooking, mopping, vacuuming, dusting, washing and ironing, showed a significantly lowered incidence of breast cancer, both before and after menopause.

The reason, scientists believe, is that household chores carried out daily act as sustained, regular moderate exercise. The fall in incidence of breast cancer among this category of women is considerable – around 30 per cent – and is marked even when compared to those who take more vigorous but less frequent formal exercise.

GO COLD-WATER SWIMMING

Icelanders are a healthy bunch, living on average until the age of 83. It could be their unique fish-heavy cuisine, their genetic inheritance or their country's low pollution levels. Or it could be that so many of them indulge in a regular cold-water outdoor swim.

Wild water swimming has a growing fan base in other parts of Europe, with proponents typically sporting hardy, ruddy complexions and youthful looks. Now there's science to back up their enthusiasm.

A team of scientists in the Czech Republic submitted a group of hapless volunteers to an hour-long cold-water dip, three times a week, and discovered that the act of being submerged in cold water does valuable things to the immune system, shocking it into stepping up the white blood count. But cold-water swimming goes beyond a simple dip – regular sessions keep your blood pumping, sending it to the organs and churning out feel-good endorphins, as well as burning extra calories.

EAT
TURMERIC

SIR MICHAEL CAINE SWEARS BY IT: TURMERIC, LONG BELIEVED TO HAVE MYRIAD HEALTH BENEFITS, HAS BECOME THE FOCUS OF SEVERAL SCIENTIFIC STUDIES.

The bright yellow spice used extensively in Indian cooking contains more than three hundred compounds, including the nutrients magnesium, niacin and polyphenols, many of which have been linked to longevity. In fact, in common with other spices, turmeric carries more nutrients, gramme for gramme, than foods in any other food group. Of particular interest to scientific studies has been the ingredient in turmeric which lends it the characteristic bright yellow colour, a pigment called curcumin. Curcumin's medical properties have been proven to be wide reaching, in the treatment of rheumatoid arthritis, IBS, lung and brain disease and in a number of cancers.

So introduce an eighth of a teaspoon of turmeric into your day, adding it to soups, stews, curries and mayonnaise dressings. Mixed with a good few grinds of black pepper, you will be enabling your liver and digestive system. Cooked turmeric offers a different range of health benefits to raw (you can buy the spice in powdered form or as a root, from which you could grate a quarter of an inch into your dishes).

BE CAREFUL
WHO YOU MARRY

NUMEROUS STUDIES HAVE FOUND THAT A HAPPY MARRIAGE IMPROVES MENTAL AND PHYSICAL HEALTH AND LIFE EXPECTANCY OF BOTH MEN AND WOMEN, BUT THERE ARE SEVERAL FACTORS WITHIN A MARRIAGE THAT HAVE SIGNIFICANT, THOUGH DIFFERENT, EFFECTS, DEPENDING ON YOUR GENDER.

A study of 127,545 American men found that married men live longer than single men, that those who married after the age of 25 were healthier than those who married younger, and that the longer a man stays married, the greater his life expectancy compared with single or unmarried peers.

Some would argue that healthier men are more eligible and more likely to marry than unhealthy specimens, but actually the opposite is true: unhealthy men tend to marry earlier. They are also less likely to divorce and more likely to remarry after a divorce or bereavement.

The age gap between spouses also has a significant effect. One study found that a man's chance of dying is cut by a fifth if his wife is 15 to 17 years younger than him – make of that what you will. However, a study of two million Danish couples found that women who are 7 to 9 years older than their husbands are one fifth more likely to die than women with husbands of the same age. The greater the age gap, the higher the mortality – for women.

In general, married people recover better, and faster, from illness and surgery – simply because they have someone to look after them. And married men have a better track record of visiting their GPs, having health check-ups, cutting down on the booze and taking any necessary medication. It's assumed they have their wives to thank for this, so don't underestimate the power of a little gentle nagging. Education plays its part too. The more educated a man's wife, the lower his risk of coronary heart disease, the lower his blood pressure and cholesterol, and the lower his death rate.

While it seems that men get most of the benefits, it is still better for a woman to be happily married than be a single mother, or indeed a widowed man – the two groups with the worst outlook. But of course the quality of the marriage is important too. A loving, supportive marriage can reduce the risk of anxiety and depression, whereas an unhappy, stressful marriage cancels out all the benefits, increasing obesity and mortality.

So choose carefully and you can start planning your diamond wedding anniversary now.

TIP 98

EAT
YOUR BEANS

IN ANY SURVEY OF THE WORLD'S LONGEST-LIVING POPULATIONS, ONE FOOD GROUP CROPS UP OVER AND OVER: BEANS. A GREAT SOURCE OF FIBRE AND CARBOHYDRATE, AND ONE OF THE MOST NUTRITIONALLY RICH FOODS ON THE PLANET, THE HUMBLE BEAN IS WHERE IT'S AT IF YOU'RE LOOKING TO EAT YOUR WAY TO A LONG AND HEALTHY LIFE.

Whether you eat them whole in stews, chilli and salads, or mashed in hummus and dips, the bean retains its full quota of fibre; even better, it contains both soluble fibre, to slow down your digestive system, and insoluble, which will help prevent you feeling bunged up. The bean is also great for regulating your blood sugar levels, as well as keeping your blood pressure and cholesterol at a healthier level. And for every 1 per cent reduction in your cholesterol, you're cutting your risk of heart attack by 2 per cent.

As well as delivering a healthy dose of fibre, beans are also a good source of protein, which is great news for those of us needing to shed a little weight in our quest for longevity: build beans into your daily diet and you'll feel fuller longer, helping to reduce your weight and protect your heart.

SIT ON THE FLOOR
AND THEN
GET UP AGAIN
AND THEN
SIT DOWN AGAIN

In traditional Japanese communities, the population is not only living longer, but living better into old age. The elderly populations of regions such as Okinawa are lithe and active well into their later years. As a community, they are keen gardeners and take regular walks, which goes some way towards accounting for their long-lived suppleness, but studies into exactly what makes the people of Okinawa so graceful in their senior years are pointing to something else altogether.

Okinawan homes are traditionally only sparsely furnished and generally, mealtimes are enjoyed on tatami mats on the floor. This means that in the course of every day, the family get themselves seated on the floor, and up again afterwards, over and over; one study estimates several dozen times a day. This amount of exercise, built into your ordinary routine from the earliest age and continued throughout your life, builds substantial lower and core body strength that will protect against the poor balance and frailty more commonly seen in other parts of the world.

TIP 100

GET AN INJECTION
OF
YOUNG BLOOD

IT MIGHT SOUND A LITTLE MORE CATHERINE THE GREAT THAN MAINSTREAM SCIENCE, BUT WASHING OUT YOUR CIRCULATORY SYSTEM IN OLD AGE WITH A TRANSFUSION OF YOUNG BLOOD HAS A REJUVENATING EFFECT ON THE LIVER, HEART AND MUSCLES OF THE RECIPIENT.

That's according to the results of an investigation carried out by a team at Stanford University in 2005. Conversely blood from older donors, when transfused into young recipients, had the opposite effect, apparently speeding up the ageing effect. In all cases, both donors and recipients were mice, but trials are in the process of being carried out with humans in order to establish whether mice aren't the only mammals who could benefit from an injection of young blood.

Initial studies have looked at the effects, if any, of young blood infused into patients with mild to moderate Alzheimer's. Mouse trials saw a particularly beneficial effect on old hearts when given young blood. While the scientific community awaits the results of the human trials with interest, the rest of us are left pondering whether Dracula may have had the right idea (though the wrong methods) after all.